MACMILLAN EXAMS

Ready for
Advanced

workbook with key

3rd Edition

Roy Norris

Amanda French

with Miles Hordern

with audio CD

Updated in line with Cambridge English: Advanced (CAE) 2015 revisions

Macmillan Education
4 Crinan Street
London N1 9XW
A division of Macmillan Publishers Limited

Companies and representatives throughout the world

ISBN 978-0-230-46361-5 (+key edition)
ISBN 978-0-230-46362-2 (-key edition)

Text © Roy Norris and Amanda French 2014
Additional material by Miles Hordern
Design and illustration © Macmillan Publishers Limited 2014
The authors have asserted their rights to be identified as the authors
of this work in accordance with the Copyright, Designs and Patents
Act 1988.

This edition published 2014
First edition published 2004

Designed by xen
Illustrated by Richard Duszczak, Peter Harper and Lazlo Veres.
Cover photograph by Getty Images/John Cumming
Picture research by Victoria Gaunt

Authors' acknowledgements

The authors would like to thank their families for their support and
understanding, and also the freelance editor.

The publishers would like to thank all those who participated in the
development of the project.

The authors and publishers would like to thank the following for
permission to reproduce their photographs:
Alamy/Juniors Bildarchiv GmbH p44, Alamy/incamerastock p14,
Alamy/Marmaduke St. John p13, Alamy/les polders p20; **BrandX**
p113; **Comstock Images** p117; Corbis p73, Corbis/Rune Hellestad
p85; **Getty Images**/Brad Wilson p72; **MACMILLAN AUSTRALIA**
pp128, 129; **Macmillan Publishers ltd**/Stuart Cox p125;
Imagesource pp36, 107(l), 123(r,l), 126; **Photoalto** p79; **Photodisc**
pp80, 92, 122, PhotoDisc/Getty Images pp19, 104, 125(l); **Rex
Features**/Sipa Press p9; **Superstock** p121(l,r); **Thinkstock** pp11,
27(l,r), 75, 97, 107(r), 119(l,r), 127.

The author(s) and publishers are grateful for permission to reprint the
following copyright material:
Material from article 'Top Achievement – but did boy peak too soon'
by Guy Adams, copyright © ESI Media 2011, first published in The
Independent 26.11.11, reprinted by permission of the publisher;
Material from article 'Would you want to live to 100?' by Jeremy
Laurance, copyright © ESI Media 2013, first published in The
Independent 22.01.13, reprinted by permission of the publisher;
Material from article 'What, no jet packs? Life in 2013, as predicted
in 1988' by Will Dean, copyright © ESI Media 2013, first published in
The Independent 17.03.13, reprinted by permission of the publisher;
Material from 'The House of Maps' by Peter Whitfield from
Geographical Magazine dated December 2003, reprinted by
permission of the publisher;
Material from 'A Daily Hug brings the touch of success' by Oliver
Wright, copyright © News Syndication 2002, first published in The
Times 05.04.02, reprinted by permission of the publisher;
Material from article 'Chance of a lifetime – for the marketing team:
First Choice advertises for water slide tester' by Kevin Rawlinson,
copyright © ESI Media 2013, first published in The Independent
09.01.13, reprinted by permission of the publisher;
Material from article 'Ring for Ms Jeeves' by Kate Spicer, copyright
© News Syndication 2002, first published in The Times 01.09.02,
reprinted by permission of the publisher;
Material from 'The advertising creative: Hard sell' by Leo Benedictus,
copyright © Guardian News & Media Ltd. 2010, first published in The
Guardian 29.05.10, reprinted by permission of the publisher;
Material from article 'Dutch freedom and respect allow youth to
flourish' by Isabel Conway, copyright © ESI Media 2007, first
published in The Independent 14.02.07, reprinted by permission of
the publisher;
Material from article 'He is heavy. He's my brother. Silverback gorilla
greets long lost sibling with a hug' by Richard Alleyne, copyright ©
Telegraph Media Group 2012, first published in The Daily Telegraph
16.08.12, reprinted by permission of the publisher;
Material from article 'Paws for thought' by Mary Braid, copyright
© News Syndication 2004, first published in The Sunday Times
01.02.04, reprinted by permission of the publisher;

Material from article 'Snoring' by Luisa Dillner, copyright © Guardian
News & Media Ltd. 1996, first published in the Guardian 23.01.96,
reprinted by permission of the publisher;
Material 'What makes a genius' by Malcolm Gladwell, copyright
© Dennis Publishing 2008, first published in The Week 29.11.08,
reprinted by permission of the publisher;
Material from article 'Hold the line: Overheard phone calls more
distracting than room full of people chatting' by Steve Connor,
copyright © ESI Media 2013, first published in The Independent
13.03.13, reprinted by permission of the publisher;
Material from article 'The boy who broke every rule in the book' by
Scarlett Thomas, copyright © ESI Media 2004, first published in The
Independent 29.02.04, reprinted by permission of the publisher;
Material from article 'The new way to burn fat – set yourself on fire'
by Hazel Knowles, copyright © Telegraph Media Group 2005, first
published in The Daily Telegraph 04.12.05, reprinted by permission of
the publisher;
Material from article 'It's so easy to work out' by Wanda Cash,
copyright © Telegraph Media Group 2003, first published in The Daily
Telegraph 06.02.03, reprinted by permission of the publisher;
Material from article 'The truth is out there on the net' by Clive
Thompson, copyright © Clive Thompson 2004, first published in The
New Zealand Herald 05.04.04 reprinted by permission of the author;
Material from article 'Mobile-throwing contest is too close to call' by
Tim Moore, copyright © News Syndication 2003, first published in
The Times 23.08.03, reprinted by permission of the publisher;
Material from article 'Dear luggage, wish you were here' by Mark
Hodson, copyright © News Syndication 2002, first published in The
Sunday Time 28.02.02, reprinted by permission of the publisher;
Material from article 'The revolution in the way we travel' by
Simon Calder, copyright © ESI Media 2007, first published in The
Independent 15.06.07, reprinted by permission of the publisher;
Material from article 'Home stretch: What happens when
twentysomethings move back in with their parents?' by Lena Corner,
copyright © ESI Media 2012, first published in The Independent
22.04.12, reprinted by permission of the publisher;
Material from article 'In the shadow of the Shard: Why the next
generation of skyscrapers is struggling to get off the ground' by
Oliver Bennett, copyright © ESI Media 2012, first published in The
Independent 16.03.12, reprinted by permission of the publisher;
Material from article 'Rory Bremner explains how listening to the
child-friendly Peter and the Wolf made him a classical music fan
for life' by Rory Bremner, copyright © News Syndication 2013, first
published in The Times 08.04.13, reprinted by permission of the
publisher;
Material from article 'How opera is being repackaged to appeal to
young children' by Tim Walker, copyright © ESI Media 2007, first
published in The Independent 22.03.07, reprinted by permission of
the publisher;
Material from article 'Student stands by Tammy Wynette for
geography degree' by Paul Stokes, copyright ©Telegraph Media
Group 2002, first published in The Daily Telegrpah 19.07.02,
reprinted by permission of the publisher;
Material taken from original article 'Hippo Heaven' by Mark Deeble,
February 2003 in BBC Wildlife magazine. Copyright © Immediate
Media Company Bristol Limited used with permission;
Material from article 'World's oldest dinosaur found – in a museum
storeroom' by Steve Connor, copyright © ESI Media 2012, first
published in The Independent 05.12.12, reprinted by permission of
the publisher;
Material from 'The World Without Us' by Alan Weisman (Virgin Books
2007), reprinted by permission of Random House Group UK and St
Martin's Press US;
Material from Rainforest Concern Advertisement 'We Have a Choice'
copyright © Rainforest Concern;
Material from article 'Calorie levels on food packaging 'wildly
misleading'' by Nick Collins, copyright © Telegraph Media Group
2013, first published in The Daily Telegraph 18.02.13, reprinted by
permission of the publisher;
Material from article 'Science studies why some foods are so
moreish' taken from The New Zealand Herald, copyright © PA 2013,
reprinted by permission of Press Association;
Material from article 'Backstage at the world's best hotels' by
Ben Ross, copyright © ESI Media 2012, first published in The
Independent 19.10.12, reprinted by permission of the publisher.

Printed and bound in Spain by Edelvives

2018 2017 2016 2015 2014
10 9 8 7 6 5 4 3 2

Contents

1 Aiming high

Reading and Use of English Part 8

Multiple matching

1 Read the article about the explorer Ranulph Fiennes quickly. In the article, is he mainly

  A giving advice to inexperienced explorers?

  B talking about the nature of exploration?

  C promoting adventure travel to young people?

2 For questions **1–10**, answer by choosing from the sections of the article **(A–D)**. Some of the choices may be required more than once.

In which section are the following mentioned?

an aspect of Fiennes's character that may have been unfairly highlighted	**1**
a negative effect of the growing interest in adventure travel	**2**
Fiennes's suggestion that people find increasingly unusual ways to achieve recognition	**3**
a misconception regarding the knowledge previous explorers had	**4**
Fiennes's fascination with a field in which he is fairly inexperienced	**5**
Fiennes's opinion that someone who is reasonably fit could reach the South Pole	**6**
the belief that explorers have too much respect for their own field	**7**
Fiennes's primary motivation for being an explorer	**8**
the importance given by explorers to achieving something before anyone else	**9**
a reason Fiennes gives for exploration becoming more appealing to amateurs	**10**

Is this your idea of fun?

Sir Ranulph Fiennes is the world's greatest living explorer. But now it seems an endless stream of people are conquering the South Pole or clambering up Everest. Mark MacKenzie asks him, is the exploring game becoming too easy?

A

In the field of human exploration, Sir Ranulph Fiennes's personal achievements are remarkable and his numerous expeditions to the North and South Poles have turned him into an iconic figure, the explorer's explorer. Now there are many amateurs that would follow in his footsteps and adventure travel is one of the fastest growing sectors of the travel market. This year, record numbers are expected at the base camp of Everest, in the hope of reaching the summit of the world's tallest peak. So, is the exploring game getting too easy? 'Anyone who plans carefully could get to the South Pole if they're in relatively good condition and go at the right time of year,' says Fiennes. 'I would say the same of Mount Everest. If the weather's good and you take a reasonable guide, you should be able to get up even if you've never climbed before. However, there are still plenty of expeditions the majority of the public would not be able to do. Crossing the whole continent of Antarctica unsupported, for example, your troubles only really start at the South Pole. But the urge to go to far-flung regions is innate to man,' Fiennes continues, 'and I think provided there is no ecological damage, this is fine. On Everest, though, there has been a dramatic impact in terms of litter.'

B

But with specialist companies willing to deposit increasing numbers of tourists in ever more remote locations, is exploring still a true test of character? 'The challenge is what you make of it,' says Fiennes. 'In the wrong weather, you can have the most horrendous time on reasonably easy routes.' Also lying behind the increasing numbers of extreme adventurers, says Fiennes, is the improved technology used for polar equipment. 'It's all a lot lighter now, less bulky. If you're inexperienced, that makes these journeys a lot more appealing.' Patrick Woodhead, whose young team reached the South Pole in 75 days, thinks the explorer community has a tendency to be overly reverential towards their discipline and claims his South Pole trek was a thoroughly enjoyable experience. However, in Fiennes' biography of the original Antarctic explorer, Captain Robert Falcon Scott, he implies strongly that there are those among modern explorers who remain ignorant of the debt they owe to Scott's pioneering spirit. 'People today think we knew back then that Antarctica was a continent – we didn't. On his first expedition to Antarctica in 1902, Scott made an 800-mile journey when the furthest expedition previously had been 14 miles.'

C

What is it that has driven explorers to the extremes of the Earth? 'Explorers have always had a thousand different motives,' Fiennes acknowledges. 'If I'm asked myself, I am quite clear. It's my profession and how I make an income. There are people who aren't comfortable with that. I'm supposed to say "Because it's there to be conquered." I think some people still need this image of nobility.' Such frankness has contributed to Fiennes's reputation for occasional haughtiness. On an expedition in 1971, he made the mistake of taking along a television crew. 'It meant good publicity for future expeditions,' he says, 'but they deliberately set out with the aim of showing me up as a dictator.'

D

Nevertheless, Fiennes has built his reputation on the only sort of accomplishment that matters among his peers – being first. 'When Sir Edmund Hillary first scaled Everest, he used every aid at his disposal. The next "first" then has to be the person to do it without oxygen, then the first solo ascent and so on.' So are there any true 'firsts' left? 'In part, it's the attitude of the individual,' he says. 'If something has been done, they will find their own firsts. Eventually, expeditions end up relying on gimmicks; for example, going to the South Pole on a motorbike, or on a camel and so on.' In 1992, Fiennes completed his first archaeological expedition to find the lost city of Ubar in the deserts of Oman. He admits he found the detective work intriguing, albeit a challenge for a relative amateur, and believes the possibility of making similar discoveries may increasingly occupy his time in the future. While most men his age are thinking about retirement, his appetite for adventure appears undiminished.

Vocabulary

Wordlist on page 208 of the Coursebook.

A Verb and noun collocations

Complete the sentences with one of the words from the box.

out	with	in	to	into

1 Their solar panel business ran _____ problems after a succession of wet summers in the mid-2000s.

2 Last year's police campaign to reduce the number of accidents on motorways met _____ limited success.

3 Union leaders have not ruled _____ the possibility of taking strike action.

4 Her attempt to cycle across the Sahara ended _____ failure yesterday, when she fell off her bike and broke her leg.

5 Taking on the Cup holders was no easy task, but they rose _____ the challenge and drew 1–1.

B Adjective and noun collocations

1 One of the items of vocabulary in each group is not normally used with the word in capitals. Cross out the item which does not fit. There is an example at the beginning (0).

0	distinct	~~heavy~~	remote	strong	**POSSIBILITY**
1	fair	inside	realistic	slim	**CHANCE**
2	potential	recurrent	resounding	trivial	**PROBLEM**
3	burning	daunting	exciting	fresh	**CHALLENGE**
4	hard	high	personal	poor	**MOTIVATION**
5	huge	overnight	roaring	terrible	**SUCCESS**
6	continued	dismal	inevitable	urgent	**FAILURE**
7	heated	lifelong	greatest	secret	**AMBITION**
8	major	outlying	remarkable	sporting	**ACHIEVEMENT**

2 Complete the sentences with an appropriate adjective from exercise 1. There is an example at the beginning (0).

0 I can't understand why he applied for the job; there was**n't even a** _remote_ **possibility** that he'd get it.

1 Recent corruption scandals mean that the party now stands **only a** _____ **chance of** victory in the forthcoming elections.

2 During his adolescence, serious illness was a _____ **problem**, and always seemed to strike at exam time.

3 The situation does pose **a rather** _____ **challenge**, but we will not be put off.

4 His consistently low marks seem to be both the result and the cause of _____ **motivation**.

5 The book brought her great wealth and worldwide fame, but this was **no** _____ **success**; her previous two novels had been bestsellers in her own country.

6 It was a night of _____ **failure** for British athletes, whose recent successes had given cause for great optimism.

7 As I've always said, it's been a _____ **ambition** of mine to play Hamlet, and now at last I can fulfil it.

8 Undoubtedly, the greatest _____ **achievement** of the year was Alek Schmidt's record-breaking marathon run of two hours and three minutes.

C Word formation

Don't forget!

You may need to use the negative or plural form of the noun.

Complete the sentences with an appropriate noun form of the word in capitals at the end of the sentence. There is an example at the beginning **(0)**.

0 Many people at the club are questioning the ___wisdom___ of signing the 16-year-old goalkeeper. **WISE**

1 Excessive _____ to direct sunlight should of course be avoided. **EXPOSE**

2 Councillors have once again rejected the _____ for a new multi-storey car park. **PROPOSE**

3 Management criticized the unions for their stubborn attitude and _____ in the wage negotiations. **FLEXIBLE**

4 The government is concerned at the number of unfilled _____ in the nursing profession. **VACANT**

5 There is a strong feeling within the company that greater _____ should be placed on staff development. **EMPHASIZE**

6 Failure to meet legal safety _____ has led to the temporary closure of the fairground. **REQUIRE**

7 She chose to live in Brighton because of its mild climate and _____ to London. **CLOSE**

8 There is a chronic _____ of housing in our cities. **SHORT**

9 The complete _____ of this answer shows that the candidate did not read the question carefully. **RELEVANT**

10 He achieved _____ for failing a drugs test after winning an Olympic® final. **NOTORIOUS**

Language focus

A Spelling

The following letter contains **20** spelling mistakes. Find the mistakes and correct them.

Dear Sir,

I am writting to complain about an article that apeared in the 'Winners and Loosers' section in last weekend's edition of your newspaper.

The article, wich analyses the growth of my educational publishing company, 'ABC', describes me as 'a man with surprisingly little education' and attributes my success to 'agressive ambition and a complete disregard for the wellfare of his employees'. This is, of course, totaly untrue, and althought I do not intend to justify myself or my business methods, their are one or two observations I feel I ougth to make.

Firstly, the economics degree I obtained from Bristol University speaks for itself, particularly, I feel, as I graduated with first class honours. In adition, whilst I am proud to consider myself ambitious, this is not at the expense of my staff, who would, I know, be only too pleased for you to intervue them. Indeed, they would be disappointed if they where not given the oportunity to inform your readers of their generous salary, impresive working conditions and excellent promotion prospects.

As you can imagine, your article has caused considerable pane and embarrassment, both too myself and my family, who found it extremly upsetting. I trust you will print an apology in the next edition of your newspaper, pointing out and rectifying the innacuracies in the article.

Yours faithfuly

John Austin

B   Modal verbs: *might, could, may* and *can*

 Grammar reference on page 215 of the Coursebook.

1   In **1–7**, complete the second sentence so that it has the same meaning as the first. There is an example at the beginning (**0**).

0   Would you mind lending me your pen for a moment?

May _____*I borrow your pen for a moment*_____?

1   Although he lives here, we never see him.

He may _____ .

2   They're very likely to ask you to speak French during the interview.

You may _____ .

3   Perhaps she didn't know you were married.

She might _____ .

4   He had a good chance of getting the job, but he didn't apply.

If he'd applied for the job, he could _____ .

5   I rarely use my bike these days, so it would make sense if I sold it.

I rarely use my bike these days, so I may _____ .

6   Why on earth didn't you tell me you were vegetarian?

You might _____ !

7   It's unlikely she was enjoying herself very much.

She can't _____ .

I rarely use my bike these days, so it would make sense if I sold it!

2   In **1–7**, one of the three alternatives is incorrect. Cross it out. There is an example at the beginning (**0**).

0   You ~~might not~~/*may not*/*cannot* leave until I give you permission.

1   It's not my scarf – I think it *might/could/can* be Graham's.

2   It *might/may/could* not be warm enough to eat outside tonight, but we'll keep our fingers crossed.

3   He's so lazy – he *might/may/could* at least offer to do the washing up!

4   I know you didn't want to come, but you *might/may/could* as well try and enjoy yourself now that you're here.

5   Don't run across the road like that again – you *might/may/could* have been run over!

6   It was a tough walk, but we *could/were able to/managed to* reach the end before it got dark.

7   Police are now saying that the fire *might/may/could* not have been started deliberately, although they have refused to rule out the possibility of arson entirely.

Multiple-choice cloze

For questions **1–8**, read the text below and decide which answer (**A, B, C** or **D**) best fits each gap. There is an example at the beginning (**0**).

On top of the world

In December 2011, a teenage mountaineer from California **(0)** .... the youngest person to complete one of his sport's most extravagant **(1)** .... : scaling the highest peak on each of the world's seven continents. Jordan Romero was just 15 when he **(2)** .... the summit of Vinson Massif in Antarctica.

Jordan, who grew up climbing the mountains in Big Bear Lake, just east of Los Angeles, conquered his first **(3)** .... summit, Mount Kilimanjaro, at the age of nine. At 13, he became the youngest person to **(4)** .... it to the top of Everest. He beat the previous record for the Seven Summits, which was **(5)** .... by 16-year-old British climber George Atkinson. Both teenagers sparked controversy in mountaineering **(6)** .... , with purists claiming they were too young to contribute properly to climbs, and therefore relied excessively on the support of their team-mates.

Although Jordan broadcast his achievements on the Internet, his mother **(7)** .... to comment when contacted by the press, claiming that the family was not **(8)** .... attention for his feats.

0	**A** overtook	**B** turned	**C** <u>became</u>	**D** succeeded
1	**A** successes	**B** contests	**C** challenges	**D** disputes
2	**A** achieved	**B** reached	**C** fulfilled	**D** accomplished
3	**A** major	**B** chief	**C** upper	**D** superior
4	**A** get	**B** find	**C** make	**D** work
5	**A** kept	**B** maintained	**C** broken	**D** held
6	**A** sets	**B** bands	**C** fields	**D** circles
7	**A** declined	**B** rejected	**C** denied	**D** renounced
8	**A** asking	**B** seeking	**C** paying	**D** searching

Formal letter: application

1 Read the following job advertisement, which has been taken from the Internet, and make a list of the characteristics the ideal candidate would possess.

Personal assistant to insurance executive

A dynamic PA is required to work for a very busy insurance executive. Duties include correspondence, diary management and booking travel. There will also be a great deal of contact with business people at a high level. A minimum of five years' related experience is essential.

---

2 The following is a letter of application for the job advertised in exercise **1**. In **1–15**, **two** of the alternatives can be used in each space. Cross out the alternative which **cannot** be used. There is an example at the beginning **(0)**.

---

(0) *Dear Sir/Dear Executive/Dear Sir or Madam*

I am writing in **(1)** *reply/apply/response* to your advertisement which appears on the website of the *Business Times* newspaper.

As you **(2)** *must/can/will* see from my **(3)** *enclosed/attached/enveloped* CV, I have spent the last six years working at the Tadwell branch of the Excel Insurance Company. I joined the branch as trainee secretary after leaving school and two years ago I was **(4)** *appointed/destined/promoted* to the **(5)** *place/ position/post* of office manager, in charge of a **(6)** *staff/team/number* of seven. My **(7)** *duties/chores/responsibilities* range from the day-to-day **(8)** *conduct/ management/running* of the office to staff training and new recruitment. I am also responsible for **(9)** *organizing/making/sorting* travel arrangements for management and visiting officials.

I am now interested in working in a more dynamic environment and given the experience I have **(10)** *acquired/gained/learnt* at Excel, I consider myself well equipped to **(11)** *respond to/take up/rise for* the challenge offered by the post of personal assistant. I also feel I **(12)** *have/own/possess* the necessary personal qualities to **(13)** *meet/complete/deal with* the demands of the job; I have included in the CV the contact details of my branch manager, who would be **(14)** *welcome/willing/pleased* to provide you with a character reference.

I am available for interview at any time which might be convenient to you and would be able to start work after serving out the two months' notice in my **(15)** *actual/current/present* job.

I look forward to hearing from you.

Yours faithfully

Lara Goodrich

---

3 Write your own letter of application in **220–260** words for the following job, which you have seen advertised in an English-language magazine in your country.

> **Language school receptionist**
>
> Busy and expanding language school with a reputation for professional standards and friendly service requires two receptionists for its new centre in the north of England. Successful candidates will have a genuine interest in people and be able to work under pressure. They will also be reasonably fluent in both spoken and written English. IT skills an advantage. Previous experience useful but not essential.

How to go about it

- Make notes about relevant experience, skills and personal qualities which would make you suitable for the job. Think also about your reasons for applying. Remember, you can invent information.
- Make a paragraph plan of your letter. Look back at Lara Goodrich's application; how has she organized her information into paragraphs?
- Use a range of relevant vocabulary and structures. Underline any words and expressions in Lara's application which you might find useful.

Multiple choice

You are going to read a magazine article about longevity, the long life that some people have. For questions **1–6**, choose the answer (**A**, **B**, **C** or **D**) which you think fits best according to the text.

Would you want to live to 100?

Remarkably, two in five girls born today will live for a century, and boys are close behind.
But, asks Jeremy Laurance, is longevity all it's cracked up to be?

Human beings have struggled to defeat the ageing process for millennia. From olive leaves in ancient Egypt to the alchemists' 'elixir of life', vast resources have been spent – and still are today – on tonics, potions and vitamins in the attempt to stave off the ravages of the years. Now we know the secret. Quietly, without fanfare, we are putting it to work. Life expectancy soared by 30 years in richer nations during the 20th century and shows no sign of slowing. In some countries it has increased by three months a year for the last 160 years. When the British tradition of sending a telegram from the monarch to all new centenarians began in 1917, King George V dispatched 24 celebratory messages. By 1952, the number had increased 10-fold and by 2011 it had increased almost 40-fold to nearly 10 000.

Leading economist Professor John Appleby cites the figures in the British Medical Journal and asks: 'Where will it all end?' That is an economist's question, but one that 18th century author Jonathan Swift also wanted to answer. *Gulliver's Travels* features a race of humans, the Struldbrugs, who were normal in all respects except one. Their immortality, instead of being a blessing, was a curse, because they continued to age. 'At 90, they lose their teeth and hair; they have at that age no distinction of taste, but eat and drink whatever they can get, without relish or appetite ... the question therefore was not, whether a man would choose to be always in the prime of youth, attended with prosperity and health; but how he would pass a perpetual life under all the usual disadvantages which old age brings along with it.'

In a recent article, centenarian Walter James wrote a poignant account of the deprivations of age. Though he still cooks and looks after himself, does the crossword, enjoys a glass of whisky and can recall events from his past with clarity, what he cannot recover are the sensations that accompanied the events. Recounting his sporting successes and close relationships, he notes the absence of the exhilaration that went with them. 'Perhaps the greatest loss is what it is like to be in love. I can remember the routines, the shared meals, concerts and theatres, walks in the country. But writing all this is like taking a book down from the shelf and leafing through its pages.'

Such observations are bound to make those younger wonder – is ageing, at the rate those of us fortunate enough to live comfortable lives are achieving, something to be celebrated or feared? The pace of advance is astonishing. As recently as 1980, scientists believed that age 85 would mark a natural limit for average life expectancy. In Japan that barrier was passed for women in 2007. In the UK, average life expectancy for both sexes born today is over 90. What is the secret – the elixir of life? Just better standards of living, education and healthcare is all, rather than a blend of exotic ingredients secretly distilled in a laboratory. Dull, perhaps, but marvellously true. In the early part of the last century, improvements in infant and child survival contributed most to growing life expectancy, but since the 1950s the biggest gains have been in the over-80s.

What worries most people about ageing is losing their faculties and the ability to perform the daily tasks of living – eating, dressing, bathing and getting around. The trends in this regard are worrying. The good news is that despite increases in chronic conditions such as diabetes and arthritis, earlier diagnosis and improved treatments have rendered these conditions less disabling. In the future, more of us will fall ill, but the illnesses should affect us less. The result is that we may live to see our great-grandchildren and even our great-great-grandchildren. Nevertheless, there are large differences between countries in healthy life expectancy beyond 65 – that is, years spent without disability – and the UK performs poorly compared with countries such as Italy and Belgium.

If ageing is to be celebrated we need answers to the personal, social, financial and health challenges it poses. One suggestion, proposed by Professor Kaare Christensen, of the Danish Ageing Research Centre, is to extend working lives by shortening the working week. 'The 20th century was a century of redistribution of income,' Professor Christensen says. 'The 21st century could be a century of redistribution of work. Redistribution would spread work more evenly across populations and over the ages of life. Preliminary evidence suggests that shortened working weeks over extended working lives might further contribute to increases in life expectancy and health.' Work till you are 100? Now that would deserve a celebratory telegram. How many people would welcome this opportunity is quite another matter.

1 What does the writer suggest about getting older in the first paragraph?

   A Long life is no longer seen as remarkable.

   B There is no reason to celebrate getting older.

   C Life expectancy has increased beyond our expectations.

   D Staying youthful has always been something people desired.

2 The writer refers to the novel *Gulliver's Travels* in order to

   A show how the obsession with ageing is a modern phenomenon.

   B make the point that eternal life is not necessarily a positive thing.

   C illustrate how ageing has been typically portrayed in literature.

   D compare views on ageing from previous centuries and the current one.

3 What does the writer find most moving about Walter James' situation?

   A his physical deterioration

   B his determination to be independent

   C his disconnection with emotion

   D his sense of nostalgia

4 What is the writer emphasizing in the sentence 'Dull, perhaps, but marvellously true'?

   A the unexceptional reasons that people live longer

   B the particular accuracy of recent scientific prediction

   C the common patterns of longevity in different countries

   D the objectivity of statistics for ageing populations

5 In the fifth paragraph, the writer draws a contrast between

   A the fears that people have about ageing and the eventual reality.

   B countries where the elderly enjoy healthy lives and those where they do not.

   C the physical problems older people suffered in the past compared to today.

   D attitudes towards the care of the elderly across various European countries.

6 In the final paragraph, we get the impression that the writer

   A intends to extend his career in the way Professor Christensen recommends.

   B sees no connection between the way income and work might be divided.

   C is reluctant to accept lower financial rewards for a job he is already doing.

   D is sceptical of Professor Christensen's proposal regarding a person's working life.

Vocabulary

Wordlist on page 209 of the Coursebook.

Changes

1 For questions **1–4**, complete each of the gaps with a word from the box. The verb you choose must be appropriate for the gaps in both sentences. There is an example at the beginning **(0)**.

adapted altered ~~changed~~ shifted transferred

0 a I've ___*changed*___ **my mind** – I'll have the soup instead of the prawn cocktail.

 b He ___*changed*___ **places with** Jean so that he could sit nearer the blackboard.

1 a Football star Cristiano Ronaldo was _____ from Manchester United to Real Madrid **for a fee of** £80 million.

 b I've just _____ £3000 from my current account to my savings account.

2 a When asked why he hadn't done his homework, James _____ **uncomfortably in his seat**.

 b The publishing company has _____ **its attention away from** children's literature **towards** school text books.

3 a The snow leopard has _____ **to life** at altitudes of up to 6000 metres.

 b Several of her **books** have been _____ **for television**.

4 a The jacket was a perfect fit, but I **had the trousers** _____ because they were a little too tight.

 b The new tower block has dramatically _____ **the appearance** of the town.

2 Underline the word **A**, **B**, **C** or **D** which best fits each gap.

1 He's _____ changed at all since I last saw him – he's just as lively and outgoing as he always was.

 A slightly   **B** hardly   **C** subtly   **D** nearly

2 The seat is _____ adjusted by pulling on this lever here.

 A highly   **B** fully   **C** openly   **D** easily

3 Prices vary _____ , so do shop around before you buy your barbecue.

 A widely   **B** instantly   **C** completely   **D** closely

4 In response to growing criticism, the government modified its plans for education cuts, though only very _____ .

 A barely   **B** fundamentally   **C** slightly   **D** faintly

5 To her credit, she _____ transformed the business from a string of small shops into a major international chain of department stores.

 A radically   **B** revoltingly   **C** enormously   **D** increasingly

3 Complete the sentences with one of the words from the box.

> fortunes   heart   scene   pace   condition   attitudes   direction   law

1 You should go away somewhere for the weekend. **A change of** _____ will do you good.

2 At first my parents refused to let me go off travelling on my own, but then they **had a change of** _____ .

3 After a very slow start, the car chase gives the film **a** much needed **change of** _____ .

4 In **a complete change of** _____ he gave up his job in teaching and became a farmer.

5 The win **marked a change in the** _____ of the team, which had lost its previous six games.

6 Despite the operation on his eye, there has been **no significant change in the patient's** _____ .

7 For many years, anti-smoking campaigners had **called for a change in the** _____ to make it illegal for people to smoke in bars and cafés.

8 The legalization of divorce reflected **a change in** _____ **towards** marriage.

Language focus

 Grammar reference on pages 215–216 of the Coursebook.

1 Correct the following sentences by changing the underlined word or words. You may need to write more than one word. There is an example at the beginning **(0)**.

have known

0 I <u>know</u> him since we were at school together.

1 We <u>would</u> have a parrot, but he flew away one day when I was cleaning his cage.

2 The service was terrible; when our dessert arrived, Paul still <u>ate</u> his starter!

3 I <u>have met</u> some very interesting people on my holiday last year.

4 This must be about the tenth time I <u>eat</u> in this restaurant.

5 It's a long time since we <u>don't see</u> each other.

6 It wasn't the first time she <u>was catching</u> him taking money from her purse.

7 I'd like to <u>stay</u> in London longer, but we had to get back for Sandra's wedding.

8 I wish you <u>didn't give</u> him my phone number – he phoned me three times yesterday!

9 You <u>did</u> nothing but complain since we've been here.

10 She was about <u>sitting</u> down, when she noticed the chair was broken.

2 Complete the texts with an appropriate form of the verb in brackets.

A

Derek Taylor, 87, is one of Britain's longest-serving Santas: he **(1)** _____ (put) on his red suit and white beard for over 50 years now. He believes he **(2)** _____ (manage) to hold down his job in a Rotherham department store for so long by adapting to the changing attitudes of the children he **(3)** _____ (meet) down the years. 'Back in the 1960s, children **(4)** _____ (believe) in Father Christmas totally and **(5)** _____ (ask) lots of questions, like "Where exactly do you live?" or "How do you manage to squeeze down chimneys?" Nowadays they just tell me about the presents they want. Of course, the toys they ask for **(6)** _____ (change) dramatically over the years. In the old days, if you **(7)** _____ (say) you would try and bring them the doll or roller skates they wanted, their faces **(8)** _____ (light) up. Now it's all mobile phones, computers and games consoles.'

B

I'll never forget the time I **(1)** _____ (go) to the hairdresser's way back in the 1940s for my first perm, or 'permanent wave', after I **(2)** _____ (see) a picture of Gina Lollobrigida with one in a film magazine. I **(3)** _____ (work) in a shop at the time, and I **(4)** _____ (book) an appointment for 1.30 pm on Wednesday afternoon, my half day off. **(5)** _____ (wash) and cut my hair, the hairdresser rolled it into tight and rather painful metal curlers. He then connected the curlers to wires from a machine that looked as if it **(6)** _____ (just/land) from outer space! He chose that moment to tell me he **(7)** _____ (experience) problems with the machine for the last few days and that the 'baking' procedure **(8)** _____ (take) a little longer than expected. In fact, I **(9)** _____ (spend) over six hours in the hairdresser's altogether and **(10)** _____ (not/arrive) home until well after 8 o'clock! At one point during my long ordeal, after I **(11)** _____ (sit) in the same chair for about four hours, my worried husband phoned the hairdresser's to ask what time I **(12)** _____ (leave). It was the first time I **(13)** _____ (ever/have) a perm, and I decided there and then that it **(14)** _____ (be) my last!

Reading and Use of English
Part 2

Open cloze

For questions **1–8**, read the text below and think of the word which best fits each gap. Use only **one** word in each gap. There is an example at the beginning **(0)**. Write your answers **IN CAPITAL LETTERS**.

What, no jet packs?

The usual complaint **(0)** _WHEN_ looking back at old predictions about the future is that a lot of the things promised in previous decades are **(1)** .... near coming true. Jet packs, for example, **(2)** .... have been commonly available by now. One can't help feeling disappointed. But reading a piece from 1988, in **(3)** .... the *Los Angeles Times Magazine* tries to predict life for a 2013 household, has the opposite effect. The article, written by Nicole Yorkin, who later **(4)** .... on to become a screenwriter for several science-fiction series, traces a day in the life of a fictitious family. It begins in the morning when their coffee maker turns itself on and ends **(5)** .... one of the family reading in bed on a laser disc. Meanwhile, data is stored on credit-card-sized computers that Yorkin uncannily refers to **(6)** .... 'smart cards' and films are watched on **(7)** .... are described as 'ultra-thin, high-resolution video screens'. Some things aren't quite so accurate, **(8)** .... Yorkin suggests, for example, that her futuristic family will be served by home robots.

Word formation

For questions **1–8**, read the text below. Use the word given in capitals at the end of some of the lines to form a word that fits in the gap **in the same line**. There is an example at the beginning **(0)**. Write your answers **IN CAPITAL LETTERS**.

Book review: *Walls have Ears* by Mark Mitchell

Avid **(0)** .READERS. of Mark Mitchell's critically acclaimed historical novels **READ**
will not be disappointed by his latest offering, *Walls have Ears*, a simple, but
(1) .... written tale of childhood innocence in a world of adult **BEAUTY**
corruption. Mitchell, a former history teacher, shot to fame three years ago
thanks to the television **(2)** .... of his fourth novel, *Baroque of Ages*, **ADAPT**
which followed the fortunes of two teenage siblings in seventeenth-century
Britain. Despite the author's **(3)** .... with the TV production, **SATISFY**
(4) .... Marian Blackshaw and Edek Sobera, it was a huge success and **STAR**
(5) .... of his books for children rocketed overnight as a result. **SELL**
Walls have Ears is a **(6)** .... on the central theme of *Baroque of Ages*, **VARY**
though this time set against the background of Hadrian's Wall during its
construction in the second century. The chance **(7)** .... by two young **DISCOVER**
friends of a plot to assassinate the Roman Emperor responsible for the
defensive wall turns their world upside down. The children are sworn to
secrecy, but their conscience **(8)** .... to get the better of them. **THREAT**
The book will be released on June 20th.

Key word transformation

For questions **1–6**, complete the second sentence so that it has a similar meaning to the first sentence, using the word given. **Do not change the word given.** You must use between **three** and **six** words, including the word given. There is an example at the beginning **(0)**. Write your answers **IN CAPITAL LETTERS**.

0 I haven't driven an automatic car for several years.

LAST

It's ...... *SEVERAL YEARS SINCE I LAST DROVE* ...... an automatic car.

1 This is your third warning from me this week about being late for work.

NOT

This is the third time this week I .... be late for work.

2 I always hated pasta when I was a child but now I cook it regularly.

USE

I .... pasta when I was a child but now I cook it regularly.

3 We wanted to continue our mountain trek but the weather was too bad.

LIKE

We .... on with our mountain trek but the weather was too bad.

4 I want to inform you that I was not satisfied with the standard of service in your hotel.

EXPRESS

I would .... with the standard of service in your hotel.

5 I wanted to stay in last night but my flatmate insisted we go out.

SOONER

I .... in last night but my flatmate insisted we go out.

6 Didn't you want me to tell the staff about your resignation?

RATHER

Would .... the staff know about your resignation?

Writing
Part 2

Formal and informal letter

1 Read the following two Writing Part 2 tasks.

A You have just returned from a rather unsatisfactory holiday with a tour company. A friend of yours is about to go on the same holiday. Write a **letter** to your friend explaining which aspects were not satisfactory and giving her advice on how to prepare for her holiday.

B You have just returned from a rather unsatisfactory holiday with a tour company. You have decided to write a **letter** to the tour company, explaining which aspects of the holiday were not satisfactory and making recommendations for improvements.

2 **A** and **B** below are the first half of the two letters required by the tasks. Use a more formal version of the underlined information in **A**, the informal letter, to complete the gaps in **B**, the formal letter. Write **one word** in each gap. There is an example at the beginning **(0)**.

Dear Sarah

Just <u>got back</u> from the historical tour of Rome. <u>I had a very good week</u> there–the guide, Francesca, really made it for me and I learnt <u>loads</u> about the history of Rome. She really <u>knew</u> her subject and she <u>explained</u> things so well.

So all in all I really enjoyed the holiday, but I've just written to Timson's to <u>tell</u> them about two or three things that happened when I was there. It's really a way of helping them to <u>make things better</u> for future tours – like the one you're going on next month!

<u>For one thing</u>, we never made it to Ostia because the coach broke down shortly after we <u>left</u> and the local rep <u>didn't send</u> another one to replace it. <u>Also</u>, we had three free days rather than two, because our guide suddenly fell <u>ill</u> at the end and we were left to look after ourselves. <u>One last thing</u> that'll be of particular interest to you – I only <u>found out</u> when I <u>got to</u> Rome that we had to pay to <u>get into</u> all the ancient monuments ourselves, which I thought was a bit cheeky considering the price.

That last point is certainly something for you to bear in mind when you go – make sure you …

Dear Sir or Madam

I have just **(0)** <u>returned</u> from Rome, where I spent a week on one of your historical tours. I would like to express my general **(1)** _____ with the holiday, during which I learnt a great **(2)** _____ about Rome and its history. This was largely due to the excellent work of the guide, Francesca, who impressed everyone with her **(3)** _____ and the quality of her **(4)** _____ .

I feel I should, however, draw your **(5)** _____ to a number of incidents which occurred, in the hope that this may help you to **(6)** _____ your service in future. **(7)** _____ , our planned visit to Ostia was cancelled, as the bus broke down soon after our **(8)** _____ and your local representative **(9)** _____ to send a replacement. In **(10)** _____ , our two free days became three, owing to the unexpected **(11)** _____ of our guide on the final day; once again, we were not provided with a substitute. **(12)** _____ , I was rather surprised to **(13)** _____ on my **(14)** _____ in Rome that **(15)** _____ fees to ancient monuments were not included in the price of the holiday.

As a result of my experience, I would like to make a number of recommendations for future tours.

3 Now complete each of the letters, using the following plans as a guide. You should write **100–125** words for each letter.

A Giving advice to your friend

> • costs of admission – take enough money
> • guidebook poor – buy your own
> • restaurants can be pricey – check in guidebook/ ask guide about cheap ones

B Making recommendations to Timson's

> • arrange alternative if bus breaks down, guide sick, etc
> • make ad more explicit, e.g. admission costs
> • improve guidebook (say how)

Don't forget!

- Continue each letter using the same informal or formal register.
- End each letter in an appropriate way.
- Use a wide range of language.

What to expect in the exam

In Part 2 you will be expected to write only one task type of **220–260** words.

Gapped text

You are going to read an extract from a magazine article. Six paragraphs have been removed from the extract. Choose from the paragraphs **A–G** the one that fits each gap **(1–6)**. There is one extra paragraph which you do not need to use.

The house of maps

The world of geography owes a big debt to Stanfords, suppliers of maps to the world for over 160 years. Peter Whitfield traces the company's early history.

During the winter of 1887, art critic John Ruskin wrote to a well-known London shop for help: *Gentlemen, have you any school atlas on sale at present without railroads in its maps? Of all the entirely odd stupidities of modern education, railroads in maps are infinitely the oddest to my mind.* The recipient of this rather strange appeal was the firm of Edward Stanford, the map-seller who had made himself pre-eminent in his field.

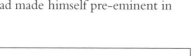

1

All this started when the first Edward Stanford launched his business in 1853, taking over the map shop of Trelawney Saunders in Charing Cross, London. He had left school at 14 to learn printing, moving on to work in a number of shops before going to work for Saunders in the map trade. Of course there were trade rivals but what put them ahead was Stanford's recognition that the 19th century was experiencing a rising demand for maps of all kinds for a variety of purposes.

2

Of the personality of the first Edward Stanford we know little, but his son, the second Edward Stanford who became head of the firm in 1882, emerges more clearly, thanks to the survival of both business and personal papers. In his business letters he made it clear that *Stanfords* was no mere shop, but a service for gentlemen governed by gentlemen. His correspondents included some of the outstanding geographers of the age, many of whom commissioned *Stanfords* to make maps for them.

3

It was under the second Stanford's direction that the firm's publishing programme reached its high point. This was the *Stanford's London Atlas of Universal Geography,* first issued in 1887, containing almost 100 detailed maps. As a textual companion to the atlas, the firm also published the magnificent *Stanford's Compendium of Geography and Travel,* a six-volume encyclopaedia of geography that was written by a team of first-class scholars.

4

This could only be of benefit to sales and the rewards were substantial. Stanford prospered, the business was entirely his own and he spent its profits freely. He sent his three sons to Oxford University, bought a large villa in a London suburb and invested in the stock exchange. This prosperity was a world away from the lowly tradesman's upbringing his father had known in the 1830s. A reversal of fortune, however, was soon to come.

5

He would have been relieved to know that all three sons survived and that the third Edward Stanford returned from the Middle East to become director of the business. But a historical and social chasm had opened up between the pre–war world and the 1920s. The family's earlier prosperity, a university education and the army had transformed the mental horizons of the Stanford children: they lost their enthusiasm for trade and preferred their lives as officers and gentlemen.

6

However, this freed *Stanfords* to concentrate on retailing instead and, finally, to take advantage of the revolution in travel that began to gather pace in the late 1960s. The package tourist heading for the beaches has little use for maps, but for the independent traveller, maps are essential companions. By importing maps from the four corners of the globe, *Stanfords* has maintained its unique role as a leader in mapping and travel literature, even though this material is no longer published by *Stanfords* itself.

A Local governors, railway or mining engineers, newspaper editors and tourists all increasingly required them, and within a few short years of his appointment at the shop, Stanford had initiated a map-publishing programme that would become the most comprehensive in England. After securing the rights to sell official maps produced by overseas and colonial survey authorities, he set about reducing all of this detailed survey information into a range of individual smaller-scale accurate and up-to date maps.

B In contrast to his dealings with these figures, there were the day-to-day arguments with resentful trade rivals and tedious officials, not to mention insolent customers. On more than one occasion Stanford writes that he is verbally abused when he asks for overdue payments.

C Alongside these achievements, the Stanford name was synonymous with the maps of Ordnance Survey but they also acted as sales agent for many other official bodies, including The Royal Geographical Society and the War Office. Its role as distributor of these official survey maps gave the business a unique status, reinforcing the perception that its own maps must be authoritative and accurate.

D Consequently, some vital energy seemed to desert the business: the golden age of Stanfords' map publishing was over, and the firm was ill-equipped to survive the years of economic depression ahead. The struggling business was eventually sold to George Philip and all Stanfords' map-making activities were absorbed into those of the parent company.

E Whether you sought an Ordnance Survey map of an English county or the goldfields of South Africa, such a reputation meant that Stanfords was always the first port of call. Over 160 years later, Stanfords continues to flourish as a map-seller, and is still renowned for its small but intriguing role in Britain's political and social history.

F The First World War was to all but eliminate the firm. Many of its staff became soldiers; private foreign travel virtually halted overnight; and all three of Stanford's sons were commissioned as junior officers. The effect was catastrophic and the strain on the ageing 'governor' proved fatal: when he died the firm was deep in debt and its future looked dark.

G This was a risk that Stanford was willing to take. Their property was rebuilt and reopened at Covent Garden with a splendid new showroom and space for all the cartographical and printing work on the floors above.

Vocabulary

Wordlist on pages 208–209 of the Coursebook.

A Adjective and noun collocations

1 Complete the crossword using the clues below. Each of the answers is a noun which collocates with the adjective in **bold**. All the collocations have appeared in Units 1–3 of the Coursebook.

Across

3 He hopes to fulfil his **burning** _____ to become world champion.

5 The kitchen was filled with the **mouth-watering** _____ of freshly baked bread.

6 Mailshots have proved to be the most **cost-effective** _____ of marketing our products.

8 The organizers claim that the demonstration was 'a **resounding** _____'.

11 It made a **welcome** _____ to win. I was getting tired of losing.

12 She now faces the **daunting** _____ of writing a successful sequel to her hugely popular first book.

Down

1 The Prime Minister yesterday announced **sweeping** _____ to her Cabinet.

2 He could smell the **acrid** _____ of rotten eggs.

4 The newspaper has been accused of publishing **misleading** _____ in relation to the case.

7 The government claims that the demonstration was 'a **dismal** _____'.

9 We still have an **outside** _____ of qualifying for the finals.

10 The pile of old clothes gave off a damp, **musty** _____ .

2 For each noun you wrote in exercise **1**, write two further adjectives which collocate with it.

B Verb and noun collocations

1 Match each of the nouns in the box to one of the groups of verbs **1–7**. All the verbs in the group must collocate with the noun. The first one has been done for you.

| information   change   a problem   a possibility   a challenge   ~~success~~   an ambition   a smell |

0 achieve	deserve	enjoy	meet with	*success*
1 achieve	fulfil	pursue	realize	_____
2 broadcast	gather	provide	publish	_____
3 face	present	rise to	take up	_____
4 bring about	call for	cope with	resist	_____
5 come up against	face up to	resolve	run into	_____
6 ignore	look into	overlook	rule out	_____
7 detect	get rid of	give off	leave	_____

2 Complete the sentences with the appropriate form of a verb from exercise **1**. There is an example at the beginning **(0)**.

0 He was a brilliant musician, who thoroughly *deserved* the **success** he had – though I don't think it made him any happier.

1 She still finds time to _____ her **ambition** to become a professional opera singer, though she is aware she may never achieve it.

2 I've been _____ **information** on minority languages for my next book.

3 The recent dramatic increase in the number of burglaries _____ a major **challenge** to the police.

4 The only way to progress is by welcoming **change**, not _____ it.

5 The company faced a number of **problems**, most of which it has now tackled and successfully _____ .

6 We're currently _____ the **possibility** of opening new premises; it depends on the company's performance over the next year.

7 It stinks of smoke in here! Could you open the window to _____ the **smell**?

C Word formation

Complete the sentences with an appropriate form of the word in capitals at the end of the sentence. There is an example at the beginning **(0)**.

Don't forget!

You may need to use the negative form of an adjective or adverb.

0 As a student, I'm still *financially* dependent on my parents. **FINANCE**

1 Unfortunately, many people are still worryingly _____ of the facts about AIDS. **IGNORE**

2 There are _____ versions of Vivaldi's *The Four Seasons*, but this recording is by far the best I've heard. **COUNT**

3 We'll have to walk to the village – it's _____ to cars. **ACCESS**

4 We have discussed these problems on _____ occasions and still nothing has been decided. **NUMBER**

5 Not _____ perhaps, sales of air conditioning systems increased considerably during the recent hot spell. **SURPRISE**

6 *Bed of Roses*, widely seen as the finest _____ work about the period, was published in 1976. **LITERATE**

7 After several _____ attempts, he finally passed his driving test in June last year. **SUCCEED**

8 A _____ study of farming procedures in fifteen African countries has just been published. **COMPARE**

9 Unemployment rose _____ last year. **DRAMA**

10 As a special _____ offer, there is a ten per cent discount on all kitchen units in the new range. **INTRODUCE**

Language focus

Grammar reference on page 216–217 of the Coursebook.

1 Complete each sentence with two words. Contractions (e.g. *haven't*, *don't*, etc) count as two words. There is an example at the beginning **(0)**.

  0 She went on holiday with her friends, though we'd rather _she had_ come with us.

  1 It was a terrible film. I wish we _____ the French one instead.

  2 She found out from Jerry, but I'd _____ told her myself.

  3 If it hadn't _____ Eleanor's excellent negotiation skills, we might never have reached an agreement.

  4 I should _____ my gloves – my hands were freezing.

  5 Most employees would prefer _____ been given a bonus rather than an expensive Christmas hamper.

  6 _____ known he intended to resign, I'd never have sacked him.

  7 If only _____ spoken to me about it before; I _____ done something to help you.

  8 The accident _____ have happened if he hadn't _____ at 90 miles an hour.

2 Tick (✔) those endings which can complete the sentences. Either one, two or all three answers are possible.

  1 I'd much rather

    A you have told me the truth.

    B I have a motorbike than a car.

    C have gone shopping on my own.

  2 If she didn't want to see you,

    A she wouldn't have invited you to her party.

    B what would you do?

    C she used to get me to tell you she wasn't at home.

  3 If it hadn't been for the rain,

    A we didn't get wet.

    B we could have eaten outside.

    C we've enjoyed ourselves very much.

  4 I couldn't have done it financially

    A if my parents hadn't supported me.

    B had it not been for the financial support of my parents.

    C without the financial support of my parents.

  5 If you push that button,

    A it goes faster.

    B you'll regret it.

    C nothing would happen.

  6 I wish I

    A would have more time to do everything.

    B had had more time to do everything.

    C had more time to do everything.

  7 If I were to lend him the money,

    A he hadn't paid it back.

    B he wouldn't have paid it back.

    C he'd have to pay it back soon.

  8 I'll tell her what you think

    A if I happen to see her.

    B should she be interested?

    C if that's alright with you.

Reading and Use of English
Part 1

Multiple-choice cloze

For questions **1–8**, read the text below and decide which answer (**A**, **B**, **C** or **D**) best fits each gap. There is an example at the beginning (**0**).

Don't forget!

Read the text through first before you start to make your choices.

Garbology

To most people, landfill sites are (**0**) .... holes in the ground where waste (**1**) .... is buried. To garbologists, however, they provide a valuable (**2**) .... of information about a population's activities in areas such as food consumption and waste disposal. Garbology is a branch of ethnography, a science which abandons traditional methods of (**3**) .... market research information, such as questionnaires and focus groups, in favour of (**4**) .... observation of people and their habits.

The world's leading garbologist, Professor William Rathje, is also an archaeologist. Archaeologists study past cultures by examining the (**5**) .... of objects and buildings, but the basic principles of archaeology can also be applied to the discarded rubbish of present-day civilizations in order to (**6**) .... a better understanding of how people behave now. Professor Rathje's work is of (**7**) .... interest to commerce; companies need to understand the lives of their consumers in order to create brands which will be of most (**8**) .... to them. Rathje's findings can help them achieve this.

0	**A** easily	**B** <u>simply</u>	**C** bluntly	**D** directly
1	**A** selection	**B** product	**C** fabric	**D** material
2	**A** spring	**B** origin	**C** source	**D** fountain
3	**A** holding	**B** meeting	**C** obtaining	**D** comprising
4	**A** near	**B** close	**C** tight	**D** hard
5	**A** rests	**B** ruins	**C** relics	**D** remains
6	**A** gain	**B** learn	**C** make	**D** gather
7	**A** high	**B** large	**C** great	**D** deep
8	**A** function	**B** serving	**C** use	**D** purpose

Reading and Use of English
Part 2

Open cloze

For questions **1–8**, read the text below and think of the word which best fits each gap. Use only one word in each gap. There is an example at the beginning (**0**).

Write your answers **IN CAPITAL LETTERS**.

Pick a number

I very (**0**) *MUCH* resent having my privacy invaded, but I would never (**1**) .... out of my way to make the lives of others difficult, (**2**) .... if they do interrupt a semi-final of the football World Cup. (**3**) .... was for this reason that I did not hang up as I heard the market researcher announce she was conducting a survey on behalf of my insurance company. (**4**) .... recently received settlement for a minor road accident, I supposed I was simply somewhere on a list of computer-generated phone calls, and just happened (**5**) .... pick up the receiver before hundreds of other insurance claimants.

I started off with good intentions and did my best to provide her (**6**) .... answers that accurately reflected my opinion. These were to be on a scale of 1 (extremely dissatisfied) to 10 (extremely satisfied). (**7**) .... , by question number nine - 'How satisfied were you with the time it (**8**) .... to process your claim?' – I had lost both interest and patience and resorted to calling out the numbers on the backs of players' shirts as they appeared on my television screen.

Review

1 Read the following Writing Part 2 task and the model answer below. Would you be interested in seeing the show which is reviewed?

You see the announcement below in a local magazine called *StageCraft*.

> There's nothing quite like live performance! And to encourage young people to attend a show we're going to publish reviews of live performances written by you. It could be a concert, play, stand-up comedy act, dance – any entertainment performed in front of a live audience.
>
> Send in your review including any relevant background, opinions about the performance and whether you would recommend it to others.

Sisters

It sounded ambitious, to say the least: a cast of more than 50 children and teenagers (all local residents), a home-grown musical score and a modest community theatre. Would *Sisters* prove to be an evening of disastrous amateur dramatics? But any doubts disappeared when the curtain went back and the entire cast performed a superbly choreographed acrobatic routine that had the audience holding their breath.

Sisters is the latest production by 'dramability' group Kaleidoscope, whose varied performances include dance, gymnastics, drama and song. Established ten years ago by Mary Pearson, largely to give her teenage daughters and their friends something to do after school, Kaleidoscope's shows now regularly sell out and their premises in an old warehouse provide a unique meeting place for young people.

The plot is straightforward: two sisters, Annie and Beth, are separated as children and, many years later, they search to be reunited. *Sisters*, however, is more about style than narrative. The song-and-dance routines set in the children's orphanage are comic, spellbinding and moving by turns. The original score, written by Mary Pearson, is particularly accomplished and the children's vocal range is enormously impressive given their age and experience.

Admittedly, the lighting team struggled with inadequate resources but such unavoidable limitations only highlighted the achievements of the players themselves. This show, filled with movement and passion, compares favourably with many professional productions. There's something for all ages here and *Sisters* shouldn't be missed.

---

2 What is the purpose of each paragraph in the model answer?
Example: Paragraph 1: *Grab the reader's attention and introduce the performance.*

3 Read the model answer again. How does the writer grab the reader's attention?

4 Make a note of the adjectives and adverbs used by the writer to express an opinion. Include any accompanying words.
Example: *superbly choreographed acrobatic routine*

Vocabulary development

5 Complete the sentences with nouns from the box.

success	interpretation	leads	timing	repertoire	acoustics	debut	casting

1 Arthur Coburg made his directorial _____ in 2004 and since that first film, he has gone from strength to strength.

2 Both Wilson and Hughes have impeccable _____; they know exactly when to pause and when to cut in, which gives their dialogue an authentic flavour.

3 The Town Hall has notoriously bad _____ , especially that echo, but visually the performance was most enjoyable.

4 The _____ was excellent, especially the choice of Tania James as Hannah.

5 The last concert was rather mixed but this one was a resounding _____ .

6 I didn't find either of the _____ particularly convincing; the supporting actors stole the show.

7 They performed some of the lesser known pieces from their _____ , which made a refreshing change.

8 His _____ of the role was most original and marks him out as an actor to watch.

Planning your review

6 You are going to write your own answer to the task in exercise **1**. Before you do, make some notes in response to the questions below.

1 How are you going to grab the reader's attention?

2 What can you say about the background to this performance? Depending on what type of performance it is, you could think about the performer(s), the setting, the plot and the creator's motivations.

3 What opinions do you have about the performance? What were its strengths and weaknesses?

4 Overall, what is your recommendation?

7 Now write your answer in **220–260** words. Remember, given the word limit, you might not be able to include all of your ideas.

Cross-text multiple matching

You are going to read commentaries by four different writers on their experience of executive burnout. For questions **1–4** on page 29, choose from the commentaries **A–D** below. The commentaries may be chosen more than once.

Time to move on?

Four writers comment on their experience of executive burnout at work.

A I would like to write a piece about the wisdom gained following my disillusionment with my work, but that would be fictitious. When I graduated, I accepted a contract with a major insurance company. During the first seven years, I steeled myself against the relentless pressure, and my achievements were recognized in every glowing performance appraisal. But when I was eventually offered a senior management position, there was an initial sense of elation and then the anti-climax. I soldiered on until it reached the point where I quite literally collapsed from exhaustion and required a period of time off work. I expected my employers to be sympathetic but I was, in essence, given an ultimatum; get back to work or move on, and it was this attitude that has left a bitter taste. Anecdotal evidence suggests mine was hardly a unique case, which makes me wonder how corporations can ever reach their productive potential.

B From the point at which I left school until my early thirties, I worked for an international bank. As most clients were operating in different time zones, you had to be available at all hours. It was physically and emotionally draining, but that's the nature of the executive lifestyle – colleagues were suffering the same degree of exhaustion. Yet with each move up the career ladder came a substantial pay rise and my ego found this irresistible. Essentially, it was my decision to tolerate the circumstances. But the time came when I simply could not face going into work anymore. I handed in my notice and the relief was immense. This gave me the opportunity to take stock and see how I could combine my passion for music with a new career. Having said all that, in a time of recession, I was one of the fortunate few that that could enjoy a lifestyle many would envy so I bear no grudge.

C That desperate phenomenon of being 'used up' by years of corporate servitude is something I knew was prevalent but never contemplated happening to me. In my case, I gave ten years of my life to a leading fashion magazine, during which time circulation figures saw a 22 per cent rise – something I feel I can take considerable credit for. I wanted our product to be the best on the market, so I often found myself unwilling to delegate tasks I knew I could do better myself. As a result, the stress was constant and burnout inevitable. In retrospect, I see how this ridiculous situation was self-inflicted – a result of my need for perfection. I took a sabbatical and finally had the mental space to reassess my priorities and myself: whereas I once regarded my obsessive qualities as a professional advantage, since then, I have made a conscious effort to suppress them. At the same time, I resent the fact that my superiors were well aware of my level of fatigue and anxiety and did nothing to alleviate it. You know then that you are a mere cog in the machine.

D For the first six years at a major PR company, I had no qualms about working extremely long hours. Then came my first child and a workload which had been feasible became overwhelming, compounded by a lack of sleep. It became apparent that I could not devote myself to the job to the degree required. Indeed, realizing my own limitations was a steep learning curve; it helped me redress the balance I needed in life and identify new priorities. I hold nothing against the company; they were entirely willing to allow me a sabbatical but I made my decision not to return within half that time. I feel that industry in general has come a long way in terms of employee welfare; there was a time when you got the sense that executives were being driven to the point of collapse, but corporate ethos appears to have changed since then.

Which writer

takes a similar view to writer C regarding their responsibility for their experiences? `1` ☐

expresses a different opinion from the others on the way their experience contributed to their personal development? `2` ☐

shares writer A's attitude towards the companies that formerly employed them? `3` ☐

has a different view from the others on the extent to which burnout is endemic within business? `4` ☐

Verb + noun collocations

1 Complete the sentences with a noun from the box.

credit	effort	grudge	notice	potential	qualms	taste	way

1 Management's insensitive handling of redundancies has **left a bitter** _____ in the mouths of many long-serving employees. (A)

2 We aim to get the best out of our employees and encourage them to **reach their** _____ . (A)

3 Don't **hand in your** _____ here without having another job to go to: make sure you have a firm job offer before resigning. (B)

4 It's not like Lucy to **bear a** _____ , but you can understand her resentment at the way she was treated by her bosses. (B)

5 I came up with the original idea, but it's the design team who should **take** _____ **for** the final product; without them it would never have been a success. (C)

6 The company has **made a conscious** _____ **to** minimize its impact on the environment. (C)

7 The architect spent just two months on the project but he **had no** _____ **about** requesting a seven-figure payment; in fact, he seemed upset when we questioned it. (D)

8 The construction industry has **come a long** _____ **in terms of** safety but there are still far too many accidents occurring each year. (D)

2 Check your answers in the reading text on page 28. The letters in brackets refer to the relevant sections of the text.

Compound nouns

Complete the sentences with a noun from the box then check your answers in the relevant section of the reading text. The letters in brackets refer to the relevant sections of the text.

career	learning	management	pay	performance

1 After a succession of **glowing** _____ **appraisals,** she was finally promoted to the **senior** _____ **position** she so clearly deserved. (A)

2 My brother and I are very different; he does not share my ambition and has absolutely no desire to **move up the** _____ **ladder.** (B)

3 Having been promised a **substantial** _____ **rise,** employees were furious to discover that their salaries had been frozen. (B)

4 She had no training or experience so at the beginning it was a very **steep** _____ **curve**, but she seems on top of the job now. (D)

Vocabulary

Wordlist on page 210 of the Coursebook.

A Body idioms

1 Complete the body idioms with words from the box. You may need to use a word more than once.

brains eye face head knees nose feet foot

1 Angela **put** her supervisor's _____ **out of joint** last week; instead of consulting him, she **went over his** _____ and spoke directly to the manager. Her supervisor was furious.

2 Tim **got off on the wrong** _____ with his new boss by daring to contradict her on his first day in the company. He doesn't **see** _____ **to** _____ **with** his line manager either; they disagree on almost everything.

3 'Can I **pick your** _____? You know a lot about banks. Which ones are offering the best deals on loans at the moment?'
'I'm not sure. I can't tell you **off the top of my** _____ . I'll have to check.'

4 Lynda only started up the company two months ago, so she's still **finding her** _____ . But she**'s got a good** _____ **for business** and I'm sure she'll do well.

5 It's pretty obvious you like the new boss. It**'s written all over your** _____, Hannah. He only has to say 'hello' to you and you **go weak at the** _____.

2 Match the idioms in exercise **1** with the meanings **a–j.**
a from memory and without checking
b start a relationship badly
c annoy someone
d be good at things relating to business
e be affected by a strong emotion
f disagree with someone
g be obvious from one's expression
h go to a person with more authority in order to get what you want
i become familiar with and confident in a new situation
j ask someone who knows a lot about a subject for information or an opinion

B Time

Complete the sentences with one of the words from the box.

at aside for of in to out on off up

1 Sorry, I can't stop to chat – I'm a little **pressed** _____ **time**.
2 We had hoped to discuss the matter in the meeting but we **ran** _____ **of time**.
3 I always try to **set** _____ **some time** each day to read the newspaper.
4 We have a huge garden, which **takes** _____ **most of my free time**.
5 Not many people have heard of her, but **it's only a matter** _____ **time before** she becomes famous.
6 I did as much as I could _____ **the time available**.
7 We didn't arrange to meet _____ **any specific time**, but he should be here by now.
8 He is retiring from his post in order to **devote more time** _____ his family.
9 She gets straight to the point; she doesn't like to **waste time** _____ small talk.
10 All pregnant women have the right to **take time** _____ **work** for antenatal care.

Language focus

 Grammar reference on page 218 of the Coursebook.

A Gerunds and infinitives

Complete the second sentence so that it has a similar meaning to the first sentence. Use the word given, without changing it in any way. There is an example at the beginning (0).

0 She will often panic if there is a problem.

TENDENCY

She _____ *has a tendency to panic if there is a problem* _____ .

1 I was surprised when he said he wouldn't work overtime.

REFUSAL

His _____ .

2 Don't bother to read that book.

WORTH

It _____ .

3 Shall I carry your bag for you?

LIKE

Would _____ ?

4 He tried very hard to give up junk food.

EFFORT

He _____ .

5 I'm very grateful to you for coming at such short notice.

APPRECIATE

I really _____ .

6 I found it impossible not to laugh when he said that.

HELP

I _____ .

7 If you don't leave now, you'll miss the bus.

BETTER

You _____ .

8 I find it difficult to remember names.

DIFFICULTY

I _____ .

9 They made us clean up the mess.

MADE

We _____ .

10 She didn't like the fact that he had been treated so badly.

BEING

She objected _____ .

B Punctuation

Each line in the following article contains a punctuation mistake. Correct the mistakes. There is an example at the beginning (0).

                                        its

0 A heating company near Birmingham has introduced group hugs to ~~it's~~ workforce

1 in a drive to boost staff morale. Since, employees at Farrelly Engineering started

2 hugging first thing in the morning and last thing at night; profits have more than

3 doubled Now the firm is introducing other initiatives, including soothing music

4 and regular nights' out at company expense. The idea came after Jerry Farrelly,

5 the director went on a motivational course in an attempt to improve morale. He

6 explained, that while many of his staff were suspicious at first, they soon came to

7 appreciate the regime. Often new staff raise their eyebrows when they see what

8 goes on, but we have found they soon get into the mood,' he said. Padma Mistry

9 who works in the accounts-department, commented on the difference between the

10 attitudes of men and women, 'The girls decided among themselves to start hugging

11 each other,' she explained. 'The men dont want to join in, but they have tried to

12 shake each others hands each day. A hug is a superb start to the day. We never

13 argue now as everything is so relaxed. Its a really fun place to work.' Rob Carter,

14 who has worked for the firm for five years said he used to work long hours and get

15 very stressed. However that's all changed. 'It may sound strange, but I actually look

16 forward to going in to work on Monday now, he confessed.'

Reading and Use of English
Part 1

Multiple-choice cloze

For questions **1–8**, read the text below and decide which answer (**A**, **B**, **C** or **D**) best fits each gap. There is an example at the beginning (**0**).

Dream job?

A holiday company is advertising a 'dream job' as a waterslide tester **(0)** ...... someone with the opportunity to earn £20 000 a year. The advertisement joins a list of job offers which just happen to be **(1)** ...... by a detailed press release. Remember when a job as the 'caretaker' of one of the world's most beautiful island paradises **(2)** ...... the news? Charity worker Ben Southall reportedly **(3)** ...... 35 000 applicants and, even before he was **(4)** ...... as the winner, the head of Tourism Queensland said the stunt had **(5)** ...... the organization £55m. One airline passenger who complained about the quality of the in-flight food was given a job as a taster by Virgin Airlines, although it is perhaps a **(6)** ...... of opinion whether that meets the criteria for 'dream job'.

The holiday company says that shortlisted applicants will be taken to a water park to **(7)** ...... who gets the job and that the successful candidate will **(8)** ...... slides based on the 'adrenalin factor', as well as share their experiences via social media.

0 A offering	**B** giving	**C** <u>providing</u>	**D** inviting
1 A attended	**B** supplemented	**C** combined	**D** accompanied
2 A made	**B** filled	**C** attracted	**D** involved
3 A challenged	**B** overcame	**C** beat	**D** opposed
4 A awarded	**B** announced	**C** stated	**D** claimed
5 A earned	**B** gained	**C** acquired	**D** profited
6 A case	**B** matter	**C** sense	**D** point
7 A influence	**B** elect	**C** figure	**D** determine
8 A value	**B** rate	**C** regard	**D** qualify

Reading and
Use of English
Part 2

Open cloze

For questions **1–8**, read the text below and think of the word which best fits each gap. Use only **one** word in each gap. There is an example at the beginning **(0)**. Write your answers **IN CAPITAL LETTERS**.

Don't forget!

- Read the text through first before you start to make your choices.
- The emphasis is on grammatical words, such as prepositions, auxiliary verbs and articles.

Female butlers

A new breed of butlers has appeared the scene; increasingly, it seems **(0)** ..*THE*.. rich and famous are turning **(1)** .... women to perform the little domestic duties of everyday life. But **(2)** .... female butlers are in ever greater demand, they are also in short supply. Ivor Spencer, who runs the most traditional **(3)** .... the well-known butler schools, has trained only eight women in 21 years. Even at the more progressive butler academies fewer than one in four trainees is female.

Butlerine Sarah Whittle says that women are in demand because they're less stuffy than men. 'We're better **(4)** .... picking up on people's moods,' she says. 'And we can organize several things at **(5)** .... : it's in our nature to multitask.' Whittle **(6)** .... expected to be smart and professional **(7)** .... duty, but she does get glamorous perks – presents of chocolate, champagne and, on one occasion, an expensive pair of shoes. But the job has its downsides. Hundred-hour weeks are **(8)** .... uncommon, the hours are unsociable and the tasks often less than glamorous.

Reading and
Use of English
Part 3

Word formation

For questions **1–8** read the text below. Use the word given in capitals at the end of some of the lines to form a word that fits in the gap **in the same line**. There is an example at the beginning **(0)**. Write your answers **IN CAPITAL LETTERS**.

Sales manager

As part of its major new programme of **(0)** ..*EXPANSION*.. , RAL	**EXPAND**
Cosmetics is seeking to appoint a dynamic sales professional to	
run a team of sales **(1)** .... in the UK.	**REPRESENT**
You will be highly-motivated, with the drive and **(2)**	**DETERMINE**
to be the best in your field. You will also have strong **(3)**	**LEAD**
qualities and be an effective communicator. The position will	
involve frequent travel to Europe for **(4)** .... at	**ATTEND**
international sales conferences, as well as training courses at our	
head office in Lyon. Priority will be given to those **(5)**	**APPLY**
who can demonstrate a good working knowledge of French.	
Previous experience in the cosmetics industry is **(6)**	**PREFER**
though not essential. We guarantee a comprehensive and	
(7) .... remuneration package, including a company car,	**COMPETE**
private health insurance and a contributory pension scheme. If you	
feel you have the necessary qualities and background, send your CV	
to Alain Sylvestre, 22 rue Marivaux, 69142 Lyon, France. Closing date	
for **(8)** .... of applications: September 25th.	**RECEIVE**

Reports

1 Read the following Writing Part 2 task.

An international research group is carrying out an investigation into changing trends in the way young people spend their free time. You have been asked to write a report about the situation in your country. You should:

- describe the changes that have taken place over the last twenty years in the way that young people spend their free time
- say whether these changes have been for the better or the worse
- suggest how you think the situation might develop in the future.

Write your **report** in **220–260** words.

2 The following report was written in answer to the task above by a British person in the mid-1960s. Put the paragraphs in the correct order, using the underlined words to help you. Then write a suitable heading for each paragraph.

Young people's leisure time activities

1 _____

The growth in popularity of the car has made once popular pastimes rather dangerous. Street games such as football, skipping or marbles are no longer such a common sight. Similarly, cycling on the open road is becoming less attractive, particularly with the construction of motorways, which began at the end of the last decade. Sadly, youngsters now spend more time in the home, where another invention has radically transformed their habits.

2 _____

The main difference between now and twenty years ago is the increased wealth and greater amount of free time available to young people. This, in itself, represents a welcome change, but two other developments have restricted the nature and quality of leisure time activities.

3 _____

It is highly likely that television will continue to dominate the lives of our youth in the years to come. Teenagers and people in their twenties may well spend most of their spare time at home, simply watching TV programmes or listening to their latest long-playing records. They might even begin to wish they had less free time on their hands.

4 _____

The purpose of this report is to comment on recent changes in the way young people make use of their spare time in my country and to consider possible future trends.

5 _____

Where previously whole families would gather round the radio to listen to a gripping drama, now children fight with their parents over which of the two television channels they should select. Courting couples rarely go ballroom dancing or join long queues outside cinemas and music halls as they once did; instead, they stay in to watch television or perhaps worse, attend wild pop concerts or parties, where they dance in uncontrolled ways.

3   Find examples in the model of the following:

Language used to compare the past and the present	Different ways of referring to young people
e.g. *once popular pastimes*	e.g. *youngsters*
Language used to make future predictions	**Different ways of referring to free time**
e.g. *It is highly likely that television will continue …*	

4   Underline those words and expressions which express the writer's opinion on whether the changes have been for the better or the worse.

Example: This, in itself, represents a welcome change …

5   The writer of the report uses a consistently formal register. Sometimes, this involves using nouns rather than verbs. For each of the following, find the equivalent expression in the model answer.

a The car has become more and more popular …

_____

b … especially because they've built motorways …

_____

c … young people have more money and more free time.

_____

Useful language	**Don't forget!**
Refer to the following sections in the Wordlist of the Coursebook: • Possibility: page 208 • Change: page 209	• Plan your answer before you write. • Use a consistently formal register. • Link one paragraph with the next, as in the model. • Give your report a title and each of your paragraphs a heading.

6   Now write your own answer to the question on page 34.

Gapped text

1 You are going to read an extract from an article about the partnership between two people who work as advertising creatives. Choose from the paragraphs **A–G** on page 37, the one that fits each gap **(1–6)**. There is one extra paragraph which you do not need to use.

A creative partnership

Finding the right partner was the most important part of Laurent Simon and Aidan McClure's careers as advertising creatives – and yes, as they tell Leo Benedictus, it is like a marriage.

Down the hall I follow a man in uniform through a complex of photographic studios. And there, in the loud white room where he releases me, is a milling group of stylists, models and photographers. Everyone is striving to realize the vision of two advertising creatives – Laurent Simon and Aidan McClure. But I can't tell you what that vision is because this is part of their presentation for winning new business, and news, in London's ad land, travels fast.

1

It's probably for this reason that McClure is eyeing the notebook where I have been jotting all the confidential details. We agree to move downstairs. McClure and Simon admit that, given all the time they spend together tussling over new ideas, they see far more of one another than they do of their girlfriends.

2

Finding a partner, therefore, is scarcely less fraught than choosing a husband or a wife. 'It was quite an emotional rollercoaster,' McClure remembers from their days at college. 'There's this mad scramble where everyone tries to find a partner. Then normally those partners don't work out. So you have all these break-ups. And they can be quite messy, because one person wants to break up, but the other person thought everything was fine.'

3

Simon says that it still is but McClure vehemently disagrees. 'So then we met in a pub and we were like "Shall we give

it a go? Shall we not?" And we decided to give it a week or so. And six years later ...' They both laugh. As is usual, one person had to be designated the 'copywriter' (McClure), and the other the 'art director' (Simon). In practice, however, the distinction is often hazy, as it is the overall concepts that really matter.

4

And, in the four years since, they have been busy, working on TV, poster, radio and newspaper campaigns for Maltesers, KFC®, Dulux and other big brands. Each job begins with a brief prepared by the agency's strategic planners, setting out what the client is trying to do. From this, Simon and McClure must conjure up a marketing idea that will accomplish it. They tend not to deal directly with the clients.

5

They must be doing it well, however, because once a team fails to be outstanding in this business, there's only one outcome. 'People get made redundant quite a fair old bit,' McClure says, scratching his head. Little wonder that the details of today's pitch matter so much. Indeed, it is probably fair to say that no industry besides advertising gives creative people so much time or money to get their ideas absolutely right.

Such harmony, I can't help feeling, must be a pleasure in itself. Though it does not always last forever. 'You see some teams that really don't get on,' McClure chuckles. 'They fight openly in front of you,' he continues, 'We had one where this team obviously hated each other and we did say, "If we ever get to that stage, it's just not worth it."' They smile, and look at each other. Simon is nodding his head in agreement. 'But luckily we haven't got to that stage,' he says.

A A young female colleague loiters nervously nearby. She asks the boys a question about the shoot, and Simon says 'Yes please' to her immediately. There is no consultation, and McClure does not correct him. It is strikingly clear that both men feel sure that they want the same thing.

B And yet, though they clearly love all these perks, it is also obvious that the work itself is what gives them the greatest satisfaction. 'It's the best job in the world.' McClure grins.

C But then it is the relationship between two 'creatives' that powers this entire industry; each creative team is hired together, briefed together, assessed together, and fired together. There are teams in London today who have been coming up with ads for 40 years or more.

D 'It's part of our job when we work on pitches, you have to keep it under your hat,' McClure explains regretfully as he shakes my hand. 'It's a small world,' his partner Simon agrees, 'so everyone knows everyone. And it's very, very competitive.'

E In this respect the two men excelled themselves, winning an award for producing the country's best student portfolio at the end of their year at college. The prize was three internships at leading agencies, one of which took them on.

F Indeed, having gone through such procedures several times, McClure and Simon found themselves the last two singletons on the prestigious Watford advertising course. 'I didn't understand Laurent, because his English was so bad,' McClure says.

G This role is taken by account executives, who act as the industry's go-betweens, smoothing out creative differences and arguing the absent party's case. Simon admits that there's a lot of joking around. 'They're always saying, "Oh you creatives, trying to do something out-of-this-world."'

Vocabulary

Wordlist on page 210 of the Coursebook.

A Adjective and noun collocations

1 Match each of the nouns in the box to one of the groups of adjectives **1–8**. All the adjectives in the group must collocate with the noun.

relationship	argument	love	feelings	family	friend	couple	tension

1 brotherly	first	true	unrequited	_____
2 inner	mixed	negative	strong	_____
3 courting	elderly	married	young	_____
4 close	love-hate	rocky	stable	_____
5 best	close	mutual	school	_____
6 adoptive	extended	immediate	single-parent	_____
7 heated	furious	fierce	pointless	_____
8 family	social	rising	heightened	_____

2 Complete the sentences with an appropriate adjective from exercise **1**.

1 I have a _____ **relationship** with my job; how I feel about it usually depends on what mood I'm in when I get to work.

2 It was a _____ **argument**: neither of us was ever likely to change the other's way of thinking.

3 Her latest novel is a tale of _____ **love**; Ross is besotted with his boss Hermione, who shows no interest in her young admirer.

4 Sandra's parents have _____ **feelings** about her going to live abroad; they want her to lead her own life, but they'd be happier if she did so closer to home.

5 We're not inviting any aunts or uncles and so on – just the _____ **family**.

6 I met Paul on holiday and he's become quite a _____ **friend**.

7 The photograph shows a young _____ **couple** speaking to a priest, probably about their forthcoming wedding.

8 Faced with mounting _____ **tension**, the government introduced a number of far-reaching political reforms.

B Verbs

Complete the sentences with the appropriate form of one of the verbs from the box. In each pair of sentences 1–4, the verb required in **a** and **b** is the same.

call	fall	take	turn

1 a The other children laughed at her, _____ **her names** and made her cry.

b Alan Kelcher was very laid-back, and let his pupils _____ **him by his first name**.

2 a I always thought that love at first sight only happened in films but I _____ **for** Jill the moment I set eyes on her.

b He _____ **out with** his father after a blazing row and hasn't spoken to him since.

3 a He had a friendly, open face and she _____ **an instant liking to** him.

b In appearance she _____ **after** her father, but she's inherited her intelligence from her mother.

4 a He was heartbroken when she _____ **down** his proposal of marriage.

b I usually _____ **to** my mother **for** help or advice: she's a better listener than my father.

Language focus

 Grammar reference on page 219 of the Coursebook.

A Relative clauses

Correct the following sentences by changing the underlined word. You should write only **one** word.

1 We thought it was horrible, so we gave it to my mother, <u>she</u> loves that kind of thing.
2 The plane took off over two hours late, <u>what</u> meant I missed my connecting flight.
3 He was criticized for giving a speech on a subject about <u>that</u> he knew very little.
4 There are two or three people in the photo <u>which</u> name I can't remember.
5 We're going back to the same hotel <u>that</u> we stayed last year.
6 I still don't understand the reason <u>because</u> they decided to close the sports centre.
7 My eldest son, <u>that</u> lives in Japan now, hardly ever comes back to visit us.
8 Kate and Steve were the only two people from work <u>to</u> came to our wedding.

B Alternatives to relative clauses

1 Infinitives with 'to' can be used:
- after words like *someone, nobody, anything*, etc.
  *There's **nothing to suggest** the crimes are connected.* (= nothing which suggests)
- to replace relative clauses containing a modal verb.
  *There are **many dishes to choose from**.* (= many dishes which you can choose from)
- after phrases like *the first, the next, the only* and superlatives.
  ***The next person to talk** will get extra homework.* (= the next person who talks)

2 Relative clauses can be reduced by using:
- a present participle.
  *Who's that **person sitting** next to your brother?* (= person who is sitting)
- a past participle.
  *The two **men arrested** in connection with the robbery have been released without charge.* (= men who were/had been arrested)

1 Which famous siblings are described in each of the following pairs of sentences?
  1 a They are not <u>the only sisters ever to play each other</u> in the final of a Wimbledon championship.
  b Serena beat Venus in the 2002, 2003 and 2009 finals, but Venus was <u>the one to win the battle of the sisters</u> in the 2008 final.
  2 a When Michael was four, his dad gave him <u>a go-kart powered by a lawnmower engine</u>.
  b After a race, Ralf was usually <u>the first to phone his mother</u>.
  3 a Some of their most famous films are *Monkey Business, Duck Soup* and *A Night at the Opera*, <u>all released in the 1930s</u>.
  b One of the five brothers 'wore' <u>a moustache painted on with black greasepaint</u>; he found it easier than glueing one on.
  4 a <u>Fans hoping to see Janet in concert</u> were disappointed to hear that she had cancelled her planned tour.
  b Michael began his musical career at the age of five as the lead singer of <u>a group comprising himself and four of his eight brothers and sisters</u>.

2 Rewrite the underlined parts of the above sentences using relative pronouns.

Example: 1 a the only sisters who have ever played each other

Multiple-choice cloze

For questions **1–8**, read the text below and decide which answer (**A**, **B**, **C** or **D**) best fits each gap. There is an example at the beginning (**0**).

Dutch children enjoy their freedom

Dutch children have just been (**0**) ...... Europe's most fortunate by a recent UNICEF survey. From a tender age, their opinions are (**1**) ...... , their wishes respected, and there is no homework until their last year in preparatory school. Some would (**2**) ...... that the tendency of Dutch society to encourage infants to experience whatever they please has (**3**) ...... a whole generation into spoilt, undisciplined brats. Others say family members are remarkably (**4**) ...... with one another, feeling free to say anything, and that the way parents (**5**) ...... with their children's anxieties means that the children are well adjusted.

Dr Gerrit Breeusma, head of development psychology at the University of Groningen, says the survey's results came as no (**6**) .... 'Children have always played a very important role in Holland but there were (**7**) ...... within families during the sixties, usually over matters of discipline,' he says. 'As a result, the generation growing up at that time have made sure they get on better with their kids.' It seems that 'Let them be free' is now the (**8**) ...... rule for child-rearing in the Netherlands.

0 **A** compared	**B** put	**C** <u>rated</u>	**D** assessed
1 **A** regarded	**B** valued	**C** recognized	**D** measured
2 **A** argue	**B** criticize	**C** defend	**D** judge
3 **A** resulted	**B** created	**C** brought	**D** turned
4 **A** alike	**B** open	**C** true	**D** careful
5 **A** empathize	**B** understand	**C** analyse	**D** handle
6 **A** doubt	**B** difference	**C** consequence	**D** surprise
7 **A** beliefs	**B** conflicts	**C** decisions	**D** contradictions
8 **A** solid	**B** iron	**C** golden	**D** fixed

Word formation

For questions **1–8**, read the text below. Use the word given in capitals at the end of some of the lines to form a word that fits in the gap **in the same line**. There is an example at the beginning (**0**). Write your answers **IN CAPITAL LETTERS**.

An emotional reunion

In (**0**) _REMARKABLE_ scenes at Longleat Safari park, a pair of gorillas who **REMARK**
were brought up together but then sent to separate zoos greeted each other
(**1**) .... with outstretched arms. Nine-year-old Alf may have felt **ENTHUSIASM**
slightly (**2**) .... at meeting his 35-stone older brother, Kesho, after **EASE**
three years apart, but any (**3**) .... was dispelled as soon as the **ANXIOUS**
gorillas were reunited. They hugged, slapped each other's backs and even
shook hands. Born at Dublin Zoo, the siblings were separated when Kesho,
13, was sent to London Zoo to take part in a (**4**) .... programme. **BREED**
Since then, Kesho has grown almost beyond (**5**) .... While living **RECOGNIZE**
with three females as the (**6**) .... male, he became the leader of the **DOMINATE**
pack and transformed from a small blackback gorilla to a silverback. Alf,
who has yet to mature, is about a third of Kesho's (**7**) .... Mark **WEIGH**
Tye, head gorilla keeper at Longleat, said: 'They were very animated and
there was a lot of rough and tumble, but not in an aggressive way. It is
quite unusual to see that sort of childlike (**8**) .... in a silverback.' **BEHAVE**

Key word transformation

For questions **1–6**, complete the second sentence so that it has a similar meaning to the first sentence, using the word given. **Do not change the word given**. You must use between **three** and **six** words, including the word given. Write your answers **IN CAPITAL LETTERS**.

1 After I emigrated, I made an effort not to lose contact with my old schoolfriends

PAINS

After I emigrated, I .... in touch with my old schoolfriends.

2 I didn't like my boss from the very first moment I met her.

INSTANT

When I first met my boss, I took .... her.

3 His constant moaning tends to irritate people.

GET

He has a .... people's nerves with his constant moaning.

4 He couldn't return the jacket to its owner because he had no idea who it belonged to.

WHOSE

He would have returned the jacket to its owner if .... was.

5 I find it hard to explain what it is I admire about him.

WHY

I find it hard to explain the .... up to him.

6 I don't like the way Sue thinks she's more important than everyone else.

STOP

I wish .... on everyone else.

Essay

1 Read the Writing Part 1 task and answer the following questions:
  a What is antisocial behaviour? Think of some examples?
  b What do the three 'opinions expressed in the seminar' mean? How do you think the opinions could be developed in the essay?

Your class has attended a seminar on what methods the government could use to reduce antisocial behaviour amongst teenagers. You have made the notes below:

Methods the government
could use to reduce antisocial
behaviour amongst teenagers

• punishment

• education

• activities

Some opinions expressed in the seminar:

'We should be looking at causes before sending people to prison.'

'Teens are more likely to listen to someone they admire.'

'Young people sometimes don't have anything to do in their area.'

Write an essay discussing **two** of the methods in your notes. You should **explain which method you think is more important** for governments to consider, **giving reasons** in support of your answer.

You may, if you wish, make use of the opinions expressed in the seminar, but you should use your own words as far as possible.

Write your **essay** in **220–260** words.

2 Now read the model answer and answer the questions.

    a Which of the three methods does the writer refer to?

    b Which method does he decide is less important and what reason does he give for this decision?

    c Which method does he decide is more important, and why?

Appropriate methods for reducing antisocial behaviour

Antisocial behaviour is becoming an increasingly common occurrence affecting many urban and suburban areas. Vandalism, graffiti and general noise disturbance can have a terrible impact on communities. The government needs to deal with this widespread problem before the situation gets even worse.

There are many people in society who support proposals for tougher sentencing. They believe that time spent behind bars or at a youth detention centre will discourage people from continuing on the 'wrong path'. However, it is simply not the case that jail time acts as a deterrent. Indeed, it is more likely to expose teenagers to more experienced criminals. Furthermore, evidence suggests that by imprisoning young people, the justice system may increase their dislike of authority. This, in turn, could result in further antisocial activity.

There is no doubt in my mind that a high incidence of anti-social behaviour is linked to boredom. A recent UK survey found that two-thirds of young people cited having 'nothing to do' as a principal reason for offending. It is therefore my firm belief that the government could tackle this issue by investing in amenities such as sports centres and skate parks where teens could spend their time more productively. Many young people are also interested in developing technical skills in areas such as music and computer programming so free or subsidized classes in these subjects would certainly be worth considering.

To conclude, any solution will involve serious financial investment. However, imprisonment is only a short-term answer whereas providing young people with a range of activities that develop their skills could have long-term benefits, not just for individuals, but for society as a whole.

---

3 Look at the underlined words and phrases in the essay. Which are used for

    a providing proof? (x2)

    b stating your own opinion (x2)

    c showing causes and results ? (x3)

    d indicating contrast ? (x2)

> **Self help**
>
> Add the expressions in exercise **3** to your vocabulary notebook.

4 The writer avoids using the same vocabulary by using synonyms or alternative phrases. Match the words **1–6** with a word or phrase expressing a similar idea **a–f**.

1 affecting		**a**	issue
2 deal with		**b**	have an impact on
3 problem		**c**	nothing to do
4 discourage		**d**	answer
5 boredom		**e**	tackle
6 solution		**f**	deterrent

5 Now read the Writing Part 1 task below.

Your class has attended a seminar on what methods the government could use to reduce the number of car accidents involving young drivers. You have made the notes below:

<u>**Methods the government could use to improve driving safety in young people**</u>

- legislation
- training
- social media campaigns

Some opinions expressed in the seminar:

'We should raise the legal age for driving.'

'Young people should be required to attend several driving courses, not just one.'

'Young people are more likely to listen to role models their own age.'

Write an essay discussing **two** of the methods in your notes. You should **explain which method you think is more important** for governments to consider, **giving reasons** in support of your answer.

You may, if you wish, make use of the opinions expressed in the seminar, but you should use your own words as far as possible.

Write your **essay** in **220–260** words.

How to go about it

- Decide which two general methods you want to discuss, e.g. legislation, training or social media campaigns.
- Decide what ideas within these two general methods you want to explore, e.g.
  legislation = issuing heavy fines, raising legal age for driving, forbidding young people to carry passengers, etc.
  training = longer period of practical training, training courses for driving in difficult conditions, etc.
  social media campaigns = using role models to campaign against speeding, interviews with the police, etc.
- Write your essay using some of the language you have seen in this writing section. Avoid repeating words and phrases.
- Make sure you support your opinion with reasons.

Multiple matching

1 Read sections **A** and **B** of the text. In these paragraphs, the writer's tone shows that she is probably

a sceptical regarding the use of dogs in the classroom.

b impressed with Henry's effect on the children.

c unconvinced that Henry is making any difference.

2 You are going to read a newspaper article about the effect of having a dog in the classroom. For questions **1–10**, choose from the sections (**A–F**). The paragraphs may be chosen more than once.

In which paragraph are the following mentioned?

a way that students can overcome their fear of making mistakes   1 ☐

the fundamental reason why dogs in general have a positive impact on people's happiness   2 ☐

a motivating reason for students to keep up with their schoolwork   3 ☐

evidence to back up the theory that dogs can improve physical well-being   4 ☐

people eventually being persuaded that a dog at school is beneficial   5 ☐

a misunderstanding concerning the way a dog is being cared for   6 ☐

the popularity of a dog not attracting negative feelings   7 ☐

a decision which was taken to avoid provoking people   8 ☐

the accusation that schools have dogs just to attract media attention   9 ☐

the criteria regarding the selection of an appropriate dog   10 ☐

Paws for thought

Buying a dog for a school isn't a barking mad idea, says Mary Braid.
Man's best friend is also a useful classroom assistant.

A

Henry is the undisputed star of Dronfield School near Sheffield. Whatever the achievements of other members of the comprehensive school, it is Henry, with his soulful eyes and glossy hair, who has hogged the limelight, appearing on television in Britain and abroad. Yet despite all the public adulation, Henry stirs up no envy or resentment among the 2000 students – in fact, they all adore him, saying the Cavalier King Charles spaniel is simply a pupil's best friend. Their teachers make even greater assertions for Henry. They say the dog, who first arrived six months ago, is a super dog, who has improved pupil behaviour and encouraged more students to focus on their academic achievement.

B

'It's hard not to drift off in a large class sometimes,' explains Andrew Wainwright, 15, who, like everyone else, is crazy about Henry. 'So when I go to catch-up classes, Henry is always in the room where they're held. He helps me focus and get on with it.' Andrew says Henry is a calming influence although he is unsure of why this might be. But he knows that there's something magical about being able to interact with Henry while he is studying. He knows that if he falls behind, that opportunity will be denied. Even doubting staff have finally been won round. Perhaps that is because Henry, who lies on the floor during staff meetings, has also had a calming influence on them.

C

Wendy Brown is Andrew's teacher. It was Brown and Julie Smart, the school counsellor, who first proposed buying a school dog. 'Julie and I grew up with dogs and we were talking one day about how looking after dogs can affect children's conduct,' says Brown. 'We did some research and discovered that the presence of pets has been shown to be therapeutic. A number of studies have found that animals improve recovery after surgery or illness and have a calming influence on people in lots of settings. Some of my kids can be a handful and some of the children Julie counsels have terrible problems.'

D

The two teachers could have plucked a dog from a rescue centre but felt that those dogs were more likely to have their own behavioural issues. What they and what troubled children needed was a stable, intelligent, people-loving animal. Step forward then puppy Henry, purchased from a local breeder. Julie looks after him after school hours – information that has pacified animal lovers who, assuming he was being kept on the premises overnight, complained to the school about Henry's treatment. 'Also, the school budget was too tight to buy a dog and you can imagine that putting one before books might have stirred some people up a bit. We wanted the least controversy possible so we settled on approaching local churches. They donated the funds to buy him and his favourite food.'

E

Could the school dog become a craze? Other schools such as the Mulberry Bush, a primary school for 36 children with behavioural problems, have stepped forward to point out they already have one. Rosie Johnston, a Mulberry staff member, first brought her golden retriever, Muskoka, into school when he was nine weeks old. That was three years ago. Aside from being a calming influence, Muskoka even plays his part in literacy lessons. Children at the school can be too shy to read to adults so they read to Muskoka. 'Their anxiety about mispronouncing something or getting the words in the wrong order is reduced when they read to him,' says Johnston.

F

Psychologist Dr Deborah Wells from Queen's University Belfast specializes in animal–human interaction. She believes the underlying key to the Henry effect is that dogs offer unconditional love and that cheers up adults and children and helps with self-esteem. But traditionalist Chris Woodhead, the former chief inspector of schools says, 'I can see how children with behavioural difficulties might be helped but I'm sceptical about the use of dogs in mainstream education. I don't see why a teacher cannot create a positive learning environment through the subject they teach and their personality. Dogs strike me as a bit of a publicity stunt. It's the kind of sentimental story journalists love.' Despite this sentiment, Henry remains as popular as ever.

Vocabulary

Wordlist on page 211 of the Coursebook.

A Sleep

Complete the sentences with one of the words from the box.

off into on over from through to up

1 The neighbours had a party last night and we didn't **get** _____ **sleep** till about 3am.
2 I **stayed** _____ to watch the boxing last night – it started just after midnight.
3 Our daughter still doesn't **sleep** _____ **the night** – she always wakes up at least once.
4 She went to bed exhausted and immediately **fell** _____ **a deep sleep**.
5 The review of his performance was far from complimentary, but he wasn't going to **lose any sleep** _____ **it**.
6 I'm going to **sleep** _____ **it** tonight and I'll let you know my decision tomorrow.
7 I couldn't tell you what happened – I **nodded** _____ just before the end of the film.
8 A surprisingly high percentage of the population **suffers** _____ **insomnia**.

Self help

Study the expressions in **bold** in B for one minute. Then cover the sentence endings a–f and look only at the beginnings 1–6. How many expressions can you remember?

B Abilities

Match each sentence beginning **1–6** with an appropriate ending **a–f**.

1 This highly talented artist has **an eye**
2 Realizing he did not have **a good ear**
3 The young reporter clearly had **a nose**
4 He admits that he doesn't have **a head**
5 Dave did it himself; he is **a dab hand**
6 Being bilingual he has **a natural flair**

a **for figures**, and he leaves all the accounting work to his wife, Pam.
b **for music**, he gave up trying to learn the piano and took up acting instead.
c **for languages**, and has taught himself Russian, Greek and Polish.
d **for detail** and many of his works are mistaken for photographs.
e **for a good story** and he wrote several exclusives for the popular tabloid.
f **at DIY** and wouldn't dream of getting a builder in to do anything.

C Adjectives in film reviews

Match each of the adjectives to an appropriate description.

moving clichéd gripping over-hyped stunning excruciating innovative unconvincing

1 Both the plot and the characters were difficult to believe. _____
2 It contains some very new and original animation techniques. _____
3 We've seen this type of thing so many times before. _____
4 It had me on the edge of my seat. _____
5 It didn't live up to the expectations created by all the publicity. _____
6 Take a big box of tissues to this one – you'll need them. _____
7 Painful to watch; the most boring film of the year. _____
8 She gave an amazing performance – her most impressive yet. _____

Language focus

 Grammar reference on pages 219–220 of the Coursebook.

1 In **1–5** below, decide which sentence, **a** or **b**, follows on more naturally from the first sentence.

1 Captain John Simms, the controversial chairman of league leaders Greendale United, is in the news again.

  a The 59-year-old former ex-Army officer **has announced** his intention to cut players' wages by ten per cent if they fail to win their semi-final cup match against neighbours Bromwich City on Saturday.

  b The intention to cut players' wages by ten per cent if they fail to win their semi-final cup match against neighbours Bromwich City on Saturday **has been announced** by the 59-year-old ex-Army officer.

2 After Paris, this magnificent collection of paintings moves to the Reina Sofía Museum in Madrid, where it will remain until January.

  a A number of leading financial organizations, including two major Spanish banks and the French insurance giant ULP, which devotes one per cent of its profits to the arts, **have sponsored** the exhibition.

  b The exhibition **has been sponsored** by a number of leading financial organizations, including two major Spanish banks and the French insurance giant ULP, which devotes one per cent of its profits to the arts.

3 Annette Sawyer is the brainiest student in town!

  a The people marking her GCSE examination papers **have awarded** the sixteen-year-old from Brayton High School top marks in all eleven of her exams, a record for any pupil from Tipton, past or present.

  b The sixteen-year-old from Brayton High School **has been awarded** top marks in all eleven of her GCSE exams, a record for any pupil from Tipton, past or present.

4 The driver of a delivery van is recovering in hospital from head injuries sustained in a curious incident which occurred in the centre of Worthing yesterday.

  a Paul Roberts of Kingston Lane, Shoreham, was on his way home when he **crashed into** a lorry parked outside the main post office in Harper Street.

  b A lorry parked outside the main post office in Harper Street **was crashed into** by Paul Roberts of Kingston Lane, Shoreham, as he was on his way home.

5 Everything is done to ensure maximum comfort and relaxation for our guests during their stay at the Wilton Hotel.

  a The cleaners **do not** come in to **clean** your room until 11 am each day, so as not to disturb you.

  b Rooms **are not cleaned** until 11 am each day in order to avoid possible disturbance.

Everything is done to ensure maximum comfort and relaxation for our guests during their stay at the Wilton Hotel.

2 Complete the second sentence so that it has a similar meaning to the first sentence. There is an example at the beginning **(0)**.

0 Everyone knows she is a close friend of the prime minister.

She ___*is known to be a close friend of the prime minister*___ .

1 It is understood that the company is planning a takeover bid for its rival.

The company _____ .

2 Police say the offences took place on Monday.

The offences _____ .

3 It is believed that the injured motorcyclist was travelling at over 100 mph.

The injured _____ .

4 Experts thought that infected chickens were responsible for the outbreak of flu.

Infected chickens _____ .

5 They alleged she had lied in order to protect her boyfriend.

She _____ .

6 Someone stole my camera last weekend.

I had _____ .

7 Your eyes need testing.

You need _____ .

8 My foot became stuck in the hole.

I _____ .

Reading and Use of English
Part 2

Open cloze

For questions **1–8**, read the text below and think of the word which best fits each gap. Use only **one** word in each gap. There is an example at the beginning **(0)**. Write your answers **IN CAPITAL LETTERS**.

Snoring

Sleep deprivation can make us very angry, which is **(0)** ..WHY.. snoring – the human equivalent of a car alarm **(1)** .... set off at night – can be so irritating. Most people snore occasionally, but in middle age about 40 per cent of men and 20 per cent of women **(2)** .... so regularly. Snoring can ruin relationships and be intensely embarrassing. Snorers who go into hospital, for example, may worry that they'll keep the whole ward awake. But snoring doesn't **(3)** .... afflict the unafflicted; snorers may also disturb **(4)** .... and feel sleepy during the day.

Snoring can sometimes be a symptom of a more serious condition, such as sleep apnoea, a syndrome in **(5)** .... breathing is significantly disrupted during sleep. Some people may start off **(6)** .... uncomplicated snorers, but develop sleep apnoea as they get older. Sufferers have airways that become obstructed during sleep. Typically, they snore loudly, stop breathing, struggle **(7)** .... air, partly wake up, gulp a bit, and then recommence snoring. The cycle may **(8)** .... repeated over 100 times an hour.

Multiple-choice cloze

For questions **1–8**, read the text below and decide which answer (**A, B, C** or **D**) best fits each gap. There is an example at the beginning **(0)**.

What makes a musical genius?

In the early 1990s, the psychologist K. Anders Ericsson and two colleagues **(0)** .... themselves at Berlin's elite Academy of Music. With the help of the academy's professors, they **(1)** .... the school's violinists into three groups. First were the students with the **(2)** .... to become world-class soloists. Second were those **(3)** .... to be merely 'good'. Third were the students **(4)** .... ever to play professionally and who intended to be music teachers in schools. All were then asked how many hours they had practised since they first picked up a violin.

Everyone, from all three groups, had started playing at roughly the age of five and practised for two or three hours a week. But around the age of eight, differences started to **(5)** .... The students who would **(6)** .... as the best in their class began to practise more than everyone else, until by the age of 20 they were practising **(7)** .... over 30 hours a week. By then, the elite performers had all totalled 10 000 hours of practice over the **(8)** .... of their lives, the merely good students 8000 hours and the future music teachers just over 4000 hours.

0	**A** settled in	**B** installed	**C** set up	**D** included
1	**A** parted	**B** shared	**C** divided	**D** broke
2	**A** promise	**B** potential	**C** prodigy	**D** power
3	**A** regarded	**B** measured	**C** calculated	**D** judged
4	**A** improbable	**B** doubtful	**C** unlikely	**D** unsure
5	**A** emerge	**B** happen	**C** erupt	**D** arrive
6	**A** come out	**B** close off	**C** result in	**D** end up
7	**A** well	**B** much	**C** very	**D** far
8	**A** track	**B** way	**C** course	**D** path

Word formation

For questions **1–8**, read the text below. Use the word given in capitals at the end of some of the lines to form a word that fits in the gap **in the same line.** There is an example at the beginning **(0)**. Write your answers **IN CAPITAL LETTERS**.

Hold the line

Scientists believe they have demonstrated why mobile phone conversations seem more **(0)** ...*INTRUSIVE*... in a public place than the general noise of people talking to one another in the background.	**INTRUDE**
In a recent experiment, the **(1)** .... were asked to solve some anagram puzzles, which they were led to believe was the true	**PARTICIPATE**
(2) .... of the experiment. However, to measure their levels of	**OBJECT**
(3) .... , researchers also conducted a scripted conversation which they knew would be overheard – either between two people at the back of the room or between someone on a mobile phone and an unseen caller. Those who heard the phone conversation found it	**DISTRACT**
(4) .... more annoying but also found the content and words	**SIGNIFY**
from it much more **(5)** .... Dr Rosa Vessal, co-author of the study, believes that we may pay more attention to a cell phone	**MEMORY**
conversation because its content is **(6)** .... and we don't know where it's heading. This suggests that communal workplaces where	**PREDICT**
where people **(7)** .... make or take phone calls may suffer	**HABIT**
from reduced **(8)** .... as employees overhear these one-sided conversations.	**PRODUCE**

Proposal

1 Read the following Writing Part 2 task and the two sample answers below. Which of the versions is more likely to impress the college director? Give reasons for your answer.

Your college wishes to establish a new club for the students. The new club has the goal of 'expanding the mind'. You have been asked by the college director to propose what sort of new club should be created.

Your proposal should:

- describe the new club
- explain how it would 'expand the mind'
- suggest ways of encouraging participation.

Sample answer A

My proposal

Our college has got lots of clubs already but they're mostly for sporty types. So why don't we set up a debating club?

People have been having debates for ages – I think the Greeks started it – and it's still really useful. Basically, debaters argue with each other. But you mustn't lose your temper. You've got to think it through and try and talk people around, so you need to think about what you're going to say before you get started. Then, if you can see you've made your point, move on to the next one or you'll bore everyone rigid. So I think it's a really tricky thing to do.

I think students will come to the club. We just need to let them know about it. Why don't we choose topics that are poking fun at someone, like the teachers at the college – the students will really love that! Then I think we should stick up posters everywhere. And let's put a bit of video on the website of a funny debate. And what about giving something to the winner? People will turn up for sure if there's a prize.

So I think a debating club would be a really good idea.

Sample answer B

Proposal: A new club for the college

Introduction

Our college already boasts a wide variety of sporting and recreational clubs. However, these largely cater for physical rather than cerebral activities and that is why I propose the establishment of a debating club.

Expanding the mind

Debating is an ancient skill and one that is equally relevant today. In essence, a debate involves speakers who argue for and against a given proposition. To do this successfully they must divorce themselves from their emotions and instead present reasoned arguments in a persuasive style, a process requiring meticulous planning. This said, however, the debater must be able to deviate from the plan if they gauge that their arguments are meeting with unexpected success (or otherwise!). Thus, the debater is required to think both in advance and on their feet, a combination that requires a unique form of intellectual dexterity.

Student participation

A debating club will be well attended if we promote it in a lively way. To do this I suggest that we choose topics that are humorous or irreverent so as to engage young people. We should then put up posters around the college advertising upcoming debates. In addition, I recommend posting a short video on the college website showing an example of an entertaining debate. My final proposal is to award prizes to the winner of each event to provide a further element of competition.

Conclusion

Debating is a highbrow pastime that is enjoyable so it would be popular with the students. As such, a debating club would be a valuable addition to the college.

Language of suggestion and recommendation

2 When writing the proposal, you will need to use appropriate language to make suggestions and recommendations. Choose the correct form for each sentence below.

    1 I propose that we *setting/to set/set* up a maths club.

    2 The establishment of a history club *would/should/must* be my suggestion.

    3 I suggest *to use/using/use* social media to promote the new club.

    4 I recommend that membership of the club *was/be/will be* free for all students.

    5 My final suggestion is *to invite/invitation/inviting* other colleges to participate.

3 A successful answer will include a variety of linking words and other cohesive devices such as pronouns (*he, she, they*, etc) and demonstrative pronouns (*that, those*, etc). Look at the examples below from the introduction in Sample answer B. Then find further examples of linking words and other cohesive devices in Sample answer B.

> However, these largely cater for physical rather than cerebral activities and that is why I propose the establishment of a debating club.

- *However* introduces a contrast between the clause which follows it and the previous sentence.
- *these* refers back to sporting and recreational clubs in the previous sentence.
- *that is why* introduces a consequence of the lack of cerebral activities just mentioned.

4 Either: **a** write your own answer to the task in exercise **1** on page 50, or **b** answer the following question.

Your college wishes to establish a new club for the students. The new club has the goal of teaching and developing a practical skill. You have been asked by the college director to propose what sort of new club should be created.

Your proposal should:
- describe the new club
- explain how it would teach and develop a practical skill
- suggest ways of encouraging participation.

Write your answer in **220–260** words in an appropriate style.

Gapped text

You are going to read an extract from a magazine article. Six paragraphs have been removed from the extract. Choose from the paragraphs **A–G** on page 53 the one which fits each gap **(1–6)**. There is one extra paragraph which you do not need to use.

The boy who broke every rule in the book

Was Nicholas Culpeper a medical rebel who challenged the establishment, or simply a quack*, asks Scarlett Thomas.

Anyone who has ever used peppermint tea to ease indigestion or taken chamomile for a good night's sleep has been using herbal medicine. However suspicious some of us may be of a complete system of 'alternative' healing, we all know that, for example, vinegar is good on wasp stings, and honey helps a sore throat.

| 1 |

These are questions which have persisted for centuries. Who has the right to medical knowledge? And how could you make sure you were in safe hands? It is to the 16th century, with its complex but rather random medical system of quacks, midwives, apothecaries and a few physicians, that author Benjamin Woolley first takes us in his book *The Herbalist*. We learn of Henry VIII's answer to the problem of national regulation: the creation of the *College of Physicians*, the members of which were given licensing and fining powers – but not the power to dispense medicines, which was instead held by the apothecaries, the pharmacists of the time.

| 2 |

Although they were supposed to practise only in accordance with the *Pharmacopoeia Londinensis*, a huge book of instructions and recipes created by the *College of Physicians*, most apothecaries did not actually read Latin. This inability meant that they could not in fact read the book.

| 3 |

Even without Latin, most apothecaries had some idea of what their medicines did. And despite not understanding the Latin slurs on their characters in the *Pharmacopoeia*, the apothecaries also knew that the College had it in for them. In 1634, Nicholas Culpeper, aged 18, arrived in London with £50 in his pocket, looking for an apprenticeship. He soon became an apprentice to an apothecary, becoming familiar with long lists of

'simple' ingredients set out in the *Pharmacopoeia*, including bizarre items like human blood and earthworms.

| 4 |

So eventually abandoning his apprenticeship and despite all the rules created by the *College of Physicians*, Culpeper set up on his own as an 'independent', trading out of a shop in London's Threadneedle Street. His aim was to provide medical help for anyone who needed it and to treat people with simply prepared, locally sourced medicines. This career was interrupted by a stint as a soldier in the Civil War. It was shortly after it ended in 1649 that there was a widespread call for all legal matters to be conducted in English, so justice could be heard and understood by all.

| 5 |

When it appeared, it was twice as long as the original, bulging with additions and corrections. It also explained what the recipes were for. 'In translating the book,' Woolley notes, 'Nicholas broke every rule in it.' This was seen not just as a medical act but a deeply political one. *The College of Physicians* was outraged.

| 6 |

Was Culpeper a quack? No more so than the medical establishment of the time, argues Woolley. It was the *College's Pharmacopoeia* after all that recommended the use of the treatments based on ground gall stones of Persian goats that surely led to King Charles II's death. Yet Culpeper's legacy – the idea that medicine is not something that should be controlled by the elite but something belonging to everybody – is as important now as it was in the 17th century.

*a quack – a negative term to describe someone who pretends to possess medical knowledge and acts as a doctor

A Perhaps this was fortunate, as it warned of 'the deceit of those people who are allowed to sell the most filthy concoctions, and even mud, under the name and title of medicaments for the sake of profit'. This was undoubtedly an attack on the capabilities and moral principles of the apothecaries.

B As odd as these may seem, many recipes would call for far more extraordinary substances and objects. Culpeper did not have a good experience at this time, being assigned a new master on several occasions. Then again, this was probably not a good time for anyone to be in his position, when rules meant you could be summoned to a company 'court' for having 'stubbornness and long hair'.

C *The English Physician*, Culpeper's later book, better known as *Culpeper's Complete Herbal*, did little to pacify them. It outlined not only the uses of healing plants but also Culpeper's holistic view of medicine. Despite upsetting the establishment, it became one of the most popular and enduring books in British history.

D When things get more serious, of course, most people rush to the doctor. But what if the doctor gets it wrong? Or imagine a situation when, for whatever reasons, you wanted to find out how to use other plants to heal yourself.

E Mutual distrust and rivalry between these groups seem to have defined the medical system of the next 100 years. It wasn't until the great plague that things were shaken up. London was left almost empty of doctors, with only apothecaries still providing medical care.

F It reveals a profound insight into the trade practices of the time, and how the establishment view of who should be allowed to trade and under what conditions affected everything. This was especially true concerning the health of people denied control over their medical treatment.

G Impressed by this, Culpeper's thoughts turned to a similar democratization of medical texts. These thoughts would be made reality when he was commissioned to produce an English edition of the *Pharmacopoeia*.

2 Look at these two sentences from the text. What is the meaning of the phrasal verbs in **bold**?
[Culpeper became] familiar with long lists of 'simple' ingredients *set out* in the *Pharmacopoeia*.

[He] *set up* on his own as an 'independent', trading out of a shop in London's Threadneedle Street.

3 Match each of the phrasal verbs in sentences **1–7** with an appropriate definition **a–g**.
Example: 1 c

1 Let's stay at home – it looks as though the rain's **set in** for the day.

a delay the progress of something

2 I put on my old clothes and **set about** clearing out the garden shed.

b start doing something

3 You should aim to **set aside** at least 15 minutes each day for physical exercise.

c start and seem likely to continue

4 Strike action **set back** the building of the Olympic® stadium by several weeks.

d attack somebody

5 We **set off** at 6 in the morning and got there just before midday.

e reserve time for a specific purpose

6 It is the quality of her writing which **sets** her **apart** from other children's authors.

f make somebody different from others

7 No sooner had he jumped down into the garden than he was **set upon** by two enormous guard dogs.

g start a journey

Vocabulary

Wordlist on page 212 of the Coursebook.

A Complaints and injuries

In **1–3**, complete each gap with the correct form of one of the three words.

1 **sprain** **swell** **tear**

If your ankle becomes _____ and painful after you twist it, you may well have _____ it. This means you have stretched and possibly _____ the ligaments in your ankle.

2 **blind** **block** **upset**

I'm not coming into work tomorrow. I've got a _____ headache, a severely _____ stomach and my nose is _____ up.

3 **bruise** **chip** **dislocate**

'How did your face get _____ like that?'

'I fell over when I was ice-skating. I _____ my tooth as well. Look.'

'Nasty. The last time I went ice-skating I fell on my shoulder and _____ it.'

B Phrasal verbs

Complete the sentences with the appropriate form of one of the verbs from the box. In each pair of sentences **1–4**, the verb required for both gaps, **a** and **b**, is the same. There is an example at the beginning **(0)**.

wear	come	put	pass	bring

0 a I'd never fainted before but I _passed_ **out** when I saw all that blood.

   b Sue came to work and _passed_ her cold **on** to everyone in the office.

1 a Amy has just phoned from her sick bed – she's _____ **down with** a flu bug.

   b I'm allergic to dairy products; if I eat yoghurt, I _____ **out in** a nasty rash.

2 a He suffered a heart attack, which may have been _____ **on** by stress.

   b She was unconscious, so I _____ her **round** by throwing water over her face.

3 a My energy levels are low, and I feel _____ **out** by the end of the day.

   b The effects of the drug had soon _____ **off**, and I felt worse than I had before.

4 a I'm in agony – I tried to pick up a box of books and I _____ my back **out**.

   b She had an upset stomach, which she _____ **down to** the fish she'd eaten.

C Word formation

1 Complete the table with the infinitives of the verbs formed from the words in the box. The first two have been done for you.

s̶u̶r̶e̶	s̶t̶r̶o̶n̶g̶	courage	deaf	high	danger	deep	rich	broad	sad	force

-en	*en-*
strengthen	ensure

2 Complete the sentences using the appropriate form of the word in capitals at the end of the line. There is an example at the beginning (**0**).

0 In an effort to ____*ensure*____ **success** in next year's European competition, **SURE** United have *strengthened* their **team** by buying two outstanding **STRONG** overseas players.

1 The build-up of troops in the border area has _____ **tension** **HIGH** between the two countries.

2 Faced with a rapidly _____ economic **crisis**, the prime minister **DEEP** was coming under increasing pressure to resign.

3 Despite rocketing unemployment figures, the president insisted that there were some _____ **signs** of recovery in the economy. **COURAGE**

4 Join the World Wildlife Fund and help protect _____ **species** **DANGER** from extinction.

5 The FBI is perhaps the best known of America's **law** _____ **FORCE** **agencies**.

6 She was **deeply** _____ by the death of her cat. **SAD**

7 The school's work experience programme _____ **the outlook** **BROAD** of its pupils and greatly _____ **their lives**. **RICH**

8 His audience found the joke offensive and greeted it with a _____ **silence**. **DEAF**

Self help

Add the collocations in **bold** in exercise **2** to your vocabulary notebook.

Language focus

 Grammar reference on page 220 of the Coursebook.

Reported speech

1 Cross out the two options which cannot be used to complete each sentence. There is an example at the beginning (**0**).

0 The doctor *reassured/~~explained~~/promised/~~mentioned~~* her that the drugs would have no serious side-effects.

1 She *invited/refused/offered/asked* me to go on holiday with her.

2 David *denied/admitted/confessed/claimed* to being a little nervous before the operation.

3 We were *accused/blamed/told off/complained* for causing the disruption.

4 My mother *persuaded/encouraged/insisted/requested* I go with her to the hospital.

5 Several people have *commented/complimented/remarked/congratulated* on Sally's new look.

6 Zoe's beautician *advised/suggested/argued/warned* her against having cosmetic surgery.

7 We tried to *dissuade/discourage/urge/convince* her from going through with it, as well.

8 It has been *told/assured/announced/confirmed* that the security forces will be on maximum alert.

9 My boss could see I was stressed out and he *advised/suggested/proposed/recommended* me to take a few days' holiday.

10 She found a dead spider in her salad and *demanded/ordered/asked/insisted* to see the manager.

2 Rewrite each sentence in two different ways. In each gap you should write between two and four words. There is an example at the beginning **(0)**.

0 'I'll help you do your homework later,' she told him.

    a She said that _she would help him_ do his homework later.

    b She promised _to help him_ do his homework later.

1 'I'll cut you out of my will if you marry George,' he told his daughter.

    a He said that _____ his daughter out of his will if she married George.

    b He threatened _____ his daughter out of his will if she married George.

2 'I think you should take a few days off work,' he told me.

    a He said he _____ a few days off work.

    b He suggested _____ a few days off work.

3 'You must leave immediately!' she told them.

    a She said that _____ immediately.

    b She ordered _____ immediately.

4 'I've always loved you,' he told her.

    a He said that _____ her.

    b He confessed to _____ her.

5 'It wasn't me who stole it,' she insisted.

    a She insisted that she _____ .

    b She denied _____ .

6 There's a rumour that they paid her over €3 million for her part in the film.

    a It is rumoured that she _____ over €3 million for her part in the film.

    b She is rumoured _____ over €3 million for her part in the film.

7 'Can you take my name off the list?' he asked her.

    a He asked her if _____ his name off the list.

    b He requested that _____ be included on the list.

8 'Aliens abducted me,' he told journalists.

    a He assured journalists that he _____ by aliens.

    b He claimed to _____ by aliens.

'It wasn't me who stole it,' she insisted.

Multiple-choice cloze

For questions **1–8**, read the text below and decide which answer (**A**, **B**, **C** or **D**) best fits each gap. There is an example at the beginning (**0**).

The new way to burn fat

People who want to lose weight are being **(0)** .... a startling new way to burn fat. Would-be slimmers are flocking to a spa in Hong Kong that **(1)** .... to reduce their waistlines by smearing them with Chinese herbs, dousing them with alcohol and then **(2)** .... light to them, all for £78 a session. The spa claims that the **(3)** .... heat of the fire penetrates deep tissue, increasing circulation and helping the body to absorb the herbal concoction which works to detoxify the body and **(4)** .... down fat. It boasts that the results are **(5)** .... , with customers recording losses of up to 15 centimetres of fat after the first session.

Karen Chu, owner of The Life of Life Healing Spa in Hong Kong's busy Causeway Bay district, says that about 100 customers have successfully **(6)** .... the treatment, and there have been no **(7)** .... 'About half the customers come here for the Aqua-Fire treatment,' she said. 'It is **(8)** .... safe. You are protected from the flame by wet towels. We have never had any complaints or problems.'

0 A proposed	**B** suggested	**C** <u>offered</u>	**D** advanced
1 A predicts	**B** promises	**C** considers	**D** assures
2 A making	**B** giving	**C** holding	**D** setting
3 A soaking	**B** bitter	**C** intense	**D** forced
4 A bring	**B** take	**C** work	**D** break
5 A immediate	**B** early	**C** straight	**D** rushed
6 A undercut	**B** undergone	**C** underused	**D** undertaken
7 A casualties	**B** damages	**C** warnings	**D** cautions
8 A strongly	**B** fiercely	**C** perfectly	**D** deeply

Open cloze

For questions **1–8**, read the text below and think of the word that best fits each gap. Use only **one** word in each gap. There is an example at the beginning (**0**). Write your answers **IN CAPITAL LETTERS**.

It's easy to work out

Many people exercise **(0)** ..*WITH*... the aim of achieving a flat tummy but it isn't necessary to contort your body painfully to **(1)** .... so. Both yoga and Pilates **(2)** .... known to build amazing abdominal strength and give you greater awareness of your pelvic floor muscles. It is **(3)** .... muscles, once strengthened, that will provide greater support for vulnerable backs.

Doing crunches is one of the best ways to flatten your tummy. This involves first lying on the floor, with your hands **(4)** .... side of your head. Raise your head approximately fifteen centimetres off the ground, then pause in this position for five seconds **(5)** .... lowering it back down. You should also bend your legs, raise them and cross your ankles while doing the crunches so as to ensure that your stomach muscles do the work, **(6)** .... your back. **(7)** .... you do have back problems, using a Swiss ball when you're exercising will help protect it, too. You can place it between you and a wall, for example, and roll down it **(8)** .... you reach a squatting position.

Key word transformation

For questions **1–6**, complete the second sentence so that it has a similar meaning to the first sentence, using the word given. **Do not change the word given.** You must use between **three** and **six** words, including the word given. There is an example at the beginning **(0)**. Write your answers **IN CAPITAL LETTERS**.

0 The union leader said the crisis was caused by the banks.

ACCUSED

The union leader ......*ACCUSED THE BANKS OF CAUSING*...... the crisis.

1 Government measures of this type would be of huge benefit to us.

HUGELY

It would be .... the government took measures of this type.

2 We know that lack of sleep significantly affects your health.

HAVE

Lack of sleep is known .... your health.

3 Paul was strongly opposed to the use of his photograph for publicity purposes.

OBJECTED

Paul strongly .... used for publicity purposes.

4 One expectant mother I know demanded to have her baby at home rather than in hospital.

ON

One expectant mother I know .... birth to her baby at home rather than in hospital.

5 Lina advised me to go to a private hospital for my eye operation.

HAVE

Lina suggested .... my eye in a private hospital.

6 When I complained formally, they said they would investigate the matter further.

AGREED

When I made a .... into the matter further.

Review

1 Read the following Writing Part 2 task.

The magazine published by your English club has asked its readers to send in a review of a film or book which includes a sporting theme. Write a review for the magazine commenting on the importance of the sporting theme in the film or book and saying how well you think it is handled. You should also say why you think others might or might not enjoy seeing the film or reading the book.

2 Read the following answer, ignoring the gaps for the moment. Does the review address all parts of the task?

 # 10 years in the life of Muhammad Ali

'I AM THE GREATEST!' exclaims Will Smith in the **(1)** _____ role of this compelling film about the former world heavyweight boxing champion. But these words apply equally well to Smith's own extremely powerful acting **(2)** _____ as the man who was named sportsperson of the century in several countries including his own. Smith looks, moves and talks like the legendary boxer, and his well-deserved Oscar **(3)** _____ for Best Actor is reason enough to see the film.

Boxing is clearly central to the film, which is **(4)** _____ in the period from Ali's title-winning defeat of Sonny Liston in 1964 to his regaining of the crown from George Foreman a decade later. To the untrained eye, the boxing **(5)** _____ are entirely convincing, and succeed in conveying both the passion and the horror of the sport. The film builds up to a dramatic **(6)** _____ with the 1974 fight in Zaire, and the combination of Michael Mann's expert direction and the moving musical **(7)** _____ makes this one of the most memorable moments of the film.

But don't be put off if you're not a boxing fan – the film is as much about the social context in which the **(8)** _____ takes place as about heavyweight fights. It provides a fascinating **(9)** _____ into 1960s America and Ali's response to contemporary attitudes. It explores his relationship with the black Muslims and also shows how he risked his career and his freedom by refusing induction into the army at the time of the Vietnam War.

There's something for everyone in the film: sport, history, drama, romance and even humour. Many of the boxer's witty **(10)** _____ , particularly those delivered to journalists, will have you laughing out loud and developing an affection for one of the world's truly great sporting heroes.

3 Complete the text above with the words from the box.

> scenes performance climax lines set score insight title action nomination

4 Underline those adjectives used by the writer to express an opinion on the film or the acting. Underline any accompanying adverbs or nouns.
Example: compelling film

5 What other expressions are used by the writer to encourage readers to see the film?

6 Either: **a** write your own answer to the task in exercise **1** or **b** answer the following question:

The magazine published by your English club has asked its readers to send in a review of a film or book whose content is largely biographical. Write a review for the magazine commenting on what you learnt from the film or book and saying why you think others might or might not enjoy it.

Write your **review** in **220–260** words.

Don't forget!

- Do not write a long summary of the film or book.
- Do express your opinion throughout the review.

Before you write

In the Coursebook, read page 74 in Unit 6 and page 202 in Ready for Writing.

Reading and Use of English
Part 5

Multiple choice

1 You are going to read a magazine article. For questions **1–6**, choose the answer (**A**, **B**, **C** or **D**) which you think fits best according to the text.

The truth is out there on the Net

Far from encouraging mass deceit, the web promotes honesty because we fear getting caught, writes Clive Thompson.

Everyone tells a little white lie now and then but Cornell University professor, Jeffrey Hancock, recently claimed to have established the truth of a curious proposition: we deceive less frequently when we're online than when talking in person. He asked thirty undergraduates to record all their communications and lies for a week. Tallying the results, he found the students had mishandled the truth in about one-quarter of all face-to-face conversations, and in 37 per cent of phone calls. But once in cyberspace, only one in five instant-messaging chats contained a lie, and barely 14 per cent of email messages were dishonest. While you can't make generalizations about society solely on the basis of college students' behaviour, and recognizing there's also something odd about asking people to be honest about how often they lie, Professor Hancock's results were intriguing, not least because they upend some of our primary expectations about life on the net.

Wasn't cyberspace supposed to be the scary zone where you couldn't trust anyone? Back when the Internet first went mainstream, those pundits in the government, media and academia worried that the digital age would open the floodgates of deception. Since anyone could hide behind an anonymous chat-room nickname, net users, we were warned, would be free to lie with impunity. Parents panicked and frantically supervised their children's use of cyberspace, under the assumption that anyone lurking out there in the unknown was a threat until proved otherwise. And to a certain extent, you can see their reasoning: if we go along with the basic introduction to any psychology course, we're more likely to lie to people when there's distance between us. Eventually, though, many suspicions turned out to be unfounded.

What is it, then, about online life that makes us more truthful? It's simple: we're worried about being exposed. In 'real' life, after all, it's pretty easy to get away with deception. If you lie to someone at a party, you can always claim you said no such thing. On the Internet, your words often come back to haunt you. The digital age is tough on liars, as an endless parade of executives are finding out. This

The web promotes honesty.

isn't a problem for only corporate barons. We read the headlines; we know in cyberspace our words never die, because machines don't forget. 'It's a cut-and-paste culture,' as Professor Hancock put it, though he said that on the phone, so who knows if he really meant it? And consider that many email programs automatically 'quote' your words when someone replies to your message. Every time I finish an email message, I pause for a few seconds to reread it just to ensure I haven't said something I'll later regret.

Maybe this helps explain why television programmes like *CSI: Crime Scene Investigation* are so popular. They're all about revealing the sneaky things that people do. We watch with fascination and unease as scientists inspect the tiniest of clues – a stray hair on a car seat, a latent fingerprint. After you've seen high-tech cops rake over evidence from a crime scene with ultraviolet light and genetic sequencers enough times, you get the message: Watch out – we've got files on you. Forensic science has become the central drama of pop culture, and our fascination with it may well add to our anxieties about technology. So no wonder we're so careful to restrict our lying to low-technology environments. We have begun to be keenly suspicious of places that might be bugged, conducting all of our subterfuge in loud restaurants and lonely parks.

Still, it's not only the fear of electronic exposure that drives us to tell the truth. There's something about the Internet that encourages us to 'tell all', often in rather outrageous ways. Psychologists have noticed for years that going online seems to have a catalytic effect on people's personalities. The most quiet and reserved people may become deranged loudmouths when they sit behind the keyboard. Others conduct angry debates on discussion boards with total strangers. You can usually spot the newcomers in any discussion group because they're the ones WRITING IN CAPITALS – they're overwhelmed by the Internet's heady combination of geographic distance and pseudo-invisibility.

Our impulse to confess via cyberspace inverts much of what we think about honesty. It used to be if you wanted to really trust someone, you arranged a face-to-face meeting. Our culture still obsesses over physical contact, the shaking of hands, the lubricating chit-chat. Executives and politicians spend hours flying across the country merely for a five-minute meeting, on the assumption that even a few seconds of face time can cut through the prevarications of legal contracts. But perhaps this dependence on online communication is gratifying news. We could find ourselves living in an increasingly honest world. It will at least, inevitably, be one in which there are increasingly severe penalties for deception. With its unforgiving machine memory, the Internet might turn out to be the unlikely conscience of the world.

1 What does the writer suggest about Professor Hancock's findings?
  A They prove a higher than average level of dishonesty amongst students.
  B They are unreliable as students are not likely to have kept accurate records.
  C They only demonstrate what was already common knowledge to most people.
  D Students are less likely to lie while chatting online than on the telephone.

2 What does the writer state about the early days of internet use?
  A There was no discernible change in the general level of honest behaviour.
  B The Internet provided people with new ways to commit crime.
  C Children were frequently not permitted any kind of access to the Internet.
  D There was some over-reaction to the perceived dangers of the Internet.

3 What point is illustrated by the references to email records?
  A The corporate world has been forced to reassess its systems of communication.
  B People have developed a less trusting attitude towards others they deal with.
  C People are becoming more cautious with regard to the content of email.
  D Email and similar documentation has sometimes been used to manipulate the truth.

4 According to the writer, television programmes on forensic science have
  A led to people becoming more frightened of being exposed.
  B encouraged people to adopt more sophisticated methods of deception.
  C overtaken other types of television drama in terms of popularity.
  D given people a false impression of what science can currently achieve.

5 In the fifth paragraph, what are we told about the effect of internet chatrooms on people?
  A They have had a beneficial influence on some naturally shy people.
  B They have allowed certain people to express themselves more concisely.
  C They have led to a transformation in some people's usual behaviour.
  D They have improved relations between people from different cultures.

6 What does the writer state about the future impact of online communication?
  A People will ensure that emails are strictly accurate and honest.
  B Instances of dishonesty will have more serious consequences.
  C People will feel the need for legal advice when preparing certain documents.
  D It will remove the need for face-to-face contact.

2 Underline the following words and expressions **1–3** in the first paragraph of the text, then match each one to its definition **a–c**.

1 tell a white lie   **a** a formal word meaning *to act or speak in a dishonest way (in order to gain advantage over someone)*

2 deceive   **b** a euphemism for *to lie*

3 mishandle the truth   **c** to lie so as not to hurt someone's feelings

3 In **1–5** decide whether the words in **bold** refer to being honest (H) or dishonest (D). There is an example at the beginning **(0)**.

0 The minister for education said that the newspaper's false accusations were part of a **dirty tricks campaign** designed to harm her reputation.   *D*

1 It was a remarkably **candid confession** for a politician not normally known for his readiness to own up to his mistakes.

2 The prime minister accused his deputy of employing **underhand tactics** to gain control of the party by secretly encouraging other members to vote against him.

3 Just give me a **straight answer** to a straight question: do you intend to take the exam or not?

4 We want the advertisement to convey the message that we are a **reputable firm** of estate agents that people can trust.

5 Hobson's **devious plan** to blackmail blameless businessmen earned him the respect of the criminal underworld.

4 Which of the adjectives in **bold** in **1–5** of exercise **3** above means the following:

a dishonest and secretive

b dishonest and clever

c honest and reliable

d honest and open, especially about something difficult or painful

e honest and direct

Vocabulary

Wordlist on page 212 of the Coursebook.

A Verbs formed with *up*, *down*, *over* and *under*

1 In **1–5** below, one of the four verbs is not a real word. Cross out the verb which does not exist.

1 uproot	upgrade	uphear	update
2 overthrow	overgo	overrule	overhear
3 undercut	undertake	underroot	undergo
4 upset	uphold	upstage	uprule
5 downhold	downsize	downplay	download

2 Complete the sentences with one of the verbs from exercise **1**. There may be more than one possible answer. There is an example at the beginning **(0)**.

0 Rebels tried to _____overthrow_____ the government.

1 A higher court can _____ a judge's decision.

2 A patient may have to _____ an operation.

3 Computer users can regularly _____ their existing software.

4 A company may _____ its competitors' prices.

5 Governments sometimes _____ the seriousness of a situation.

B Adjectives formed with *in, off, on, out* and *over*

Underline the correct alternative.

1 She was momentarily blinded by the headlights of an *incoming/oncoming* **car**.

2 These research findings represent an important contribution to the *ongoing/outgoing* **debate** on the effects of passive smoking.

3 Only 30 per cent of the pupils at this school actually live in the town itself; most children come in by bus from *outdoor/outlying* **areas**.

4 First to arrive on the scene was an *off-duty/off-hand* **police officer**, who had heard the explosion from his kitchen.

5 According to some scientists, humans have only two *inborn/overnight* **fears** – fear of falling and fear of loud noises. All others, it seems, are learnt.

> **Self help**
>
> Add the adjective + noun collocations in **bold** in the above exercise to your vocabulary notebook.

C Plans

1 The following adjectives and verbs are all collocates of the nouns *plan* or *plans*. One of the items in each group is very different in meaning to the other three. Underline the odd one out. There is an example at the beginning **(0)**.

0 workable   viable   <u>controversial</u>   feasible

A controversial plan is one which causes public disagreement or disapproval; the other three adjectives are used to describe plans which are likely to succeed.

1 emergency	bold	daring	audacious
2 elaborate	detailed	intricate	devious
3 clever	ingenious	impracticable	brilliant
4 draw up	devise	carry out	conceive
5 scrap	abandon	jettison	put forward
6 shelve	announce	unveil	reveal

2 Complete the sentences with the correct form of one of the collocates you have underlined in exercise **1** above. There is an example at the beginning **(0)**.

0 Fearing they would lose votes over the issue, the government scrapped their _controversial_ plan to reintroduce military service.

1 The proposed peace plan is ill-conceived and _____ : it simply will not work.

2 Local authorities have sensibly drawn up _____ plans to be adopted in the event of further flooding.

3 It's a brilliant plan, but rather too _____ for my liking; it might lay me open to accusations of dishonesty.

4 Plans to build a nuclear power plant in the area have been _____ following strong public opposition.

5 They were prevented from _____ their plan to rob the bank after a police patrol spotted their stolen car and arrested them.

6 Management _____ a plan aimed at increasing productivity, but it was immediately rejected by union leaders.

> **Self help**
>
> Add the collocates of *plan* from exercise **1** to your vocabulary notebook.

D Amount

Match the sentence beginnings **1–6** to the endings **a–f**.

1 In the event of cancellation, a full
2 They have received such a large
3 Beach towels are provided at no extra
4 Our graphic designers have a great
5 Their advertising highlights the low
6 Overworked staff have precious little

a charge to our guests.
b cost of installation and maintenance.
c time to fulfil all their objectives.
d refund of the ticket price will be made.
e deal of experience in creating logos.
f number of orders that they cannot cope.

Language focus

 Grammar reference on pages 220–222 of the Coursebook.

A Talking about the future

Decide which answer **A**, **B**, **C** or **D** best fits each gap.

1 I hear that Brian and Julie are _____ to start a family soon.

  A projecting   **B** considering   **C** hoping   **D** assuring

2 I _____ they'll accept the offer, but it's worth a try.

  A suspect   **B** hope   **C** doubt   **D** expect

3 I'm just _____ to go out. Can I call you back later?

  A likely   **B** about   **C** almost   **D** soon

4 The company has announced that all employees _____ to receive a special bonus payment at Christmas next year.

  A arrange   **B** go   **C** are   **D** like

5 She's off sick today, but she may _____ be back at work tomorrow.

  A hardly   **B** probably   **C** unlikely   **D** well

6 Come round at 2 o'clock – we should _____ our lunch by then.

  A be finished   **B** have to finish   **C** have finished   **D** have been finishing

7 Building work is _____ to start next month, but I wouldn't be surprised if there was a delay.

  A due   **B** bound   **C** willing   **D** expecting

8 No one else thinks I'll win, but I'm pretty _____ of success myself.

  A definite   **B** confident   **C** assured   **D** doubtless

B Determiners

In each of the following sentences there is one grammatical mistake. Correct each mistake by changing or deleting one of the words in **bold**. There are two examples at the beginning **(0, 00)**.

many

0 We aren't expecting very ~~much~~ **more** people to turn up.

00 We had a ~~very~~ **lot of** problems at work today.

1 I know of **no other any** place which is quite as beautiful as this.

2 I try to go swimming **every another** day during the week – Mondays, Wednesdays and Fridays, usually.

3 **Every a few** months or so we take a day off and go walking in the mountains.

4 We only intended to spend a fortnight there, but we liked it so much we stayed for **other two** weeks.

5 *Determined* is my favourite track on the album but there are **quite a few of** others I like as well.

6 I've been working here for **quite some much** time – nearly ten years, in fact.

7 There's **no much** milk left – enough for breakfast, but that's all.

8 She's had nothing to eat for **some each three** days now – we're getting a bit worried.

Reading and Use of English
Part 2

Open cloze

For questions **1–8**, read the text below and think of the word which best fits each gap. Use only **one** word in each gap. There is an example at the beginning **(0)**. Write your answers **IN CAPITAL LETTERS**.

I think you'll find it means mobile phones.

MOBILE THROWING COMPETITION

Mobile phone throwing championships

The Mobile Phone Throwing World Championships **(0)** ..ARE.. held every year in Finland, the birthplace of the first mobile phone, which was more **(1)** .... size of a small briefcase than the tiny accessories of today. The competition is divided **(2)** .... two sections, contested by teams and individuals. The original category is judged simply on length of throw, but in the freestyle event competitors win on points awarded **(3)** .... notable performances during the run-up. **(4)** .... some competitors use their own handsets, most betray a grudging dependence on their phone **(5)** .... selecting a missile from a large range of second-hand phones supplied by the organizers.

The competition was founded by local businesswoman Christina Lund, inspired by her observations of a country tied to **(6)** .... mobiles. 'I saw that all of **(7)** .... have very different emotions about our mobiles: much of the time they cause tension and frustration. They never ring when they are supposed **(8)** .... and they go off at inconvenient times. So I had the idea of a competition based on releasing some of that tension.'

Reading and
Use of English
Part 3

Word formation

For questions **1–8**, read the text below. Use the word given in capitals at the end of some of the lines to form a word that fits in the gap **in the same line**. There is an example at the beginning **(0)**. Write your answers **IN CAPITAL LETTERS**.

Obsessed with your inbox?

It was not so long ago that we dealt with colleagues through face-to-face **(0)** ...INTERACTION... and with counterparts and customers by phone or letter. But the world of communication has **(1)** .... a dramatic transformation, not all for the good. Email, while **(2)** .... a swift means of communication, providing your server is fully functional and that the address you have contains no **(3)** .... , has had a **(4)** .... effect on certain people's behaviour, both at home and in business. For these people, the use of email has become **(5)** .... addictive, to the extent that it is **(6)** .... their mental and physical health. Addicts spend their day compulsively checking for email and have a **(7)** .... to panic if their server goes down. It is estimated that one in six people spend four hours a day sending and receiving messages, the equivalent to more than two working days a week. The negative effect on **(8)** .... is something employers are well aware of.

INTERACT
GO
DOUBT

ACCURATE
SIGNIFY
RESIST
THREAT

TEND

PRODUCE

Reading and
Use of English
Part 4

Key word transformation

For questions **1–6**, complete the second sentence so that it has a similar meaning to the first sentence, using the word given. **Do not change the word given.** You must use between **three** and **six** words, including the word given. There is an example at the beginning **(0)**. Write your answers **IN CAPITAL LETTERS**.

0 In the past, letters took ages to reach their overseas destination.

WOULD

In the past, ...IT WOULD TAKE AGES BEFORE..... letters reached their overseas destination.

1 The camera has broken at least three times.

FEWER

The camera has broken .... three occasions.

2 He is better than everyone else at creating believable characters.

SECOND

He .... it comes to creating believable characters.

3 He attended every event possible to take advantage of the conference.

MOST

He made .... attending every event possible.

4 Does your ringtone have to be quite so loud?

TURN

I wish .... your ringtone slightly.

5 John has a habit of getting angry when there isn't a good reason for it.

TEMPER

John will often .... particular reason.

6 We will install your anti-virus programme for free.

AT

The anti-virus programme .... charge.

Essay

1 Read the following Writing Part 1 task. Before you write your answer, do the related vocabulary task in exercise **2** below.

Your class has attended a panel discussion on what methods industry could use to encourage people to study science and engineering. You have made the notes below:

> **Methods industry could use to encourage people to study science and engineering.**
>
> . promote the achievements of scientists
> . subsidize training courses
> . provide schools with technology, e.g. computers

> Some opinions expressed in the discussion:
> 'The whole of society benefits from advances such as satellite technology.'
> 'It's not fair if fees are artificially lowered for some college courses and not for others.'
> 'All schools should have equal access to technology.'

Write an essay discussing **two** of the methods in your notes. You should **explain which method you think is more important** for industry to consider, **giving reasons** in support of your answer.

You may, if you wish, make use of the opinions expressed in the discussion, but you should use your own words as far as possible.

Vocabulary development: Expressing opinions

2 Complete the sentences with one of the nouns from the box. Use the collocates in **bold** to help you.

> coverage   concern   ~~priority~~   resources   action   claims   status   importance

0 This should be a **top** _priority_ in the years ahead. The council has put off taking action for too long.

1 That we are still in this predicament is a **pressing** _____ . I'm worried that in its present state the footpath is a threat to public safety.

2 This is only one of several **competing** _____ to be considered. The council must also think about parking and lighting.

3 The media **give** this topic **inadequate** _____ . It doesn't appear at all in some newspapers.

4 Scientists deserve **higher** _____ than they are **afforded** at present. Their contribution to society is seriously undervalued.

5 Many schools do not **target sufficient** _____ **at** this problem. Instead they spend their budgets buying comfortable furniture for the teachers' room!

6 Nothing now prevents the authorities from **taking immediate** _____ . The council has put off doing anything for far too long.

7 It's of **critical** _____ that industry addresses this issue. I can't understand why such a significant problem has been ignored.

3 Now write your answer in **220–260 words**.

Cross-text multiple matching

1 You are going to read four reviews of a book about travel. For questions **1–4** on page 69, choose from the reviews **A–D**. The reviews may be chosen more than once.

Crossing Paths

Four reviewers comment on writer Kerry Windham's book called Crossing Paths

A

As an acclaimed biographer of famous explorers, it was only a matter of time before Kerry Windham turned her attention to her own travels, and in her latest work she does not disappoint. In *Crossing Paths* we mount up behind Windham as she takes us on an exhilarating and often hazardous motorcycle ride around the vast territories of Australia. Unlike the continuous prose of her previous work, *Crossing Paths* is set out more as a series of encounters, each described succinctly, sometimes within a mere paragraph, and never requiring more than a few pages. Although Windham cannot claim this approach as hers alone, she does it justice by employing a frankness about her own occasional naivety which puts her in situations of jeopardy. Each unusual character she stumbles across is depicted with compassion; even while their quirks are noted, each malignant species of creature or plant is still admired for its tenacity and evolutionary genius.

B

When reading travel writing, one must be prepared to accept the overlap with fiction. In no other genre is there such an intertwining of fact with embellishment, of truth with the writer's own perception of it. That, indeed, is part of the allure; knowing that as travellers ourselves we have come home with a mythologized version of our own adventures, and recognizing this innate tendency in others. No doubt Kerry Windham has done the same with *Crossing Paths*, her account of her solo motorbike ride across the massive expanse of Australia. It is her eye for fine detail and her ability to describe it in ways that convince the reader that the memories are their own that make this tale the perfect armchair traveller's companion. An autobiographical journey is a departure from Windham's previous kinds of book, but this one is worthy of the same volume of praise.

C

In Kerry Windham's *Crossing Paths*, the fragments of her motorcycle journey through the Australian outback and isolated townships sparkle like individual jewels on a single thread. The idea of the set piece (rather than continuous narrative) owes much to *In Patagonia*, the seminal work of travel writer Bruce Chatwin. But unlike Chatwin's fictionalized anecdotes of real people and places, Windham gives us an undistorted account of her interactions with characters from all walks of life; a taciturn young station hand on a cattle ranch, an Aboriginal dreamtime healer, an 84-year-old surfer still paddling out to the beach break. Known for her writing on the exploits of earlier travellers and their epic voyages of discovery, Windham has taken a risk by reflecting on – in her own words – 'small, incidental moments' – but it has turned out to be a risk worth taking.

D

In her biographies, Kerry Windham has rightly been applauded for her inspirational prose; her pen becomes a paint brush that conveys the shades and hues, the light and the dark of her subjects, and the reader is fully present in the experience. The same mastery of technique can also be found in *Crossing Paths*, the story of her trip by bike around the Australian territories. Windham's apparent motive for embarking on this gruelling quest was to 'explore my own cultural backyard', and certainly there is much to discover. We are introduced to a diversity of people and plants, railroads and rock formations, abandoned settlements and thriving tourist towns. However, while none of these encounters lacks vividness or authenticity, there is a sense of inconsequentiality. In her other works Windham steps back and we see the full picture; in *Crossing Paths* we glimpse disassociated images.

Which reviewer

has a different opinion from the others on the overall merits of
Kerry Windham's book? 1 ☐

takes a similar view to writer C on the format of Kerry Windham's book? 2 ☐

expresses a different view from the others regarding Kerry Windham's
portrayal in the book of events as they happened? 3 ☐

shares reviewer D's opinion on the effect of Kerry Windham's use of
language in the book? 4 ☐

2 a Cover the reading text. Complete the extracts from the text **1–6** with one word. The
words are the same for **a** and **b**.

0 a ____As____ an acclaimed biographer of famous explorers, it was only a matter of
time before … (A)

  b Although Windham cannot claim this approach ____as____ hers alone, she does it
justice … (A)

1 a it was only a matter of time before Kerry Windham _____ her attention to her
own travels … (A)

  b … it has _____ out to be a risk worth taking. (C)

2 a … she takes us _____ an exhilarating and often hazardous motorcycle ride …
(A)

  b Windham has taken a risk by reflecting _____ – in her own words – 'small,
incidental moments' … (C)

3 a Unlike the continuous prose of her previous work, *Crossing Paths* is _____ out
more as a series of encounters … (A)

  b The idea of the _____ piece (rather than continuous narrative) owes much to
In Patagonia … (C)

4 a Each unusual character she stumbles _____ is depicted with compassion … (A)

  b … *Crossing Paths*, her account of her solo motorbike ride _____ the massive
expanse of Australia. (B)

5 a When reading travel writing, _____ must be prepared to accept the overlap
with fiction. (B)

  b An autobiographical journey is a departure from Windham's previous kinds of
book, but this _____ is worthy of the same volume of praise. (B)

6 a It is her eye _____ fine detail and her ability to describe it … that make this tale
the perfect armchair traveller's companion. (B)

  b Kerry Windham has rightly been applauded _____ her inspirational prose. (D)

b Now uncover the reading text and check your answers. The relevant sections are given
in brackets.

Vocabulary

Wordlist on page 212 of the Coursebook.

A Describing an adventure

1 Complete the sentences with the correct form of a verb from the box.

kick   ring   run   set   turn   win

1 Columbus did not _____ **out** to discover the New World; he was seeking a western sea route from Europe to Asia.

2 They had hardly left port when they _____ **into** a storm and had to turn back.

3 A number of shots _____ **out** and we dived under the table for cover.

4 They thought they had discovered a prehistoric burial site, but it _____ **out** to be much more recent.

5 Despite a number of setbacks, their determination _____ **through** and two of the climbers made it to the summit.

6 When she saw him lying there, she panicked momentarily, but then her first aid training _____ **in** and she began performing chest compressions on him.

2 Complete the text with a suitable word from the box.

arid   gruelling   idyllic   intrepid   swirling

It had been an extremely **(1)** _____ month-long trek across **(2)** _____ , rocky desert, but the team of **(3)** _____ explorers had refused to give in to the harsh conditions. It wasn't all scorching heat and **(4)** _____ sandstorms, however: they were able to camp for two nights at a remote oasis, a rather **(5)** _____ spot for some rest and recuperation.

B Criticism

1 The following adjectives and verbs are all collocates of the noun *criticism*. Underline the item in each group which does not express a similar meaning to the word(s) in **bold**. There is an example at the beginning **(0)**.

0 **increasing**	1 **a lot of**	2 **strong**	3 **not affected**
<u>damaging</u>	considerable	fierce	impervious to
growing	constructive	severe	unmoved by
mounting	widespread	valid	upset by

4 **give**	5 **encounter**	6 **deal successfully with**
arouse	come in for	draw
express	meet with	overcome
voice	respond to	withstand

2 Choose the correct option **A**, **B**, **C** or **D**.

1 Her _____ criticism of his work, which was based purely on her intense dislike of him, served only to undermine his self-confidence.

   A fierce   **B** valid   **C** constructive   **D** widespread

2 The president remained _____ by mounting criticism of his leadership and pressed ahead regardless with his controversial programme of policies.

   A upset   **B** unmoved   **C** impervious   **D** overcome

3 Police chiefs yesterday _____ strong criticism of a judge's decision to give a man convicted of armed robbery a six-month suspended sentence.

   A attracted   **B** met with   **C** aroused   **D** voiced

4 The decision to site the nuclear power station next to the nature reserve _____ widespread criticism from opposition politicians and environmental groups.

   A came in   **B** responded to   **C** drew   **D** expressed

C Word formation

1 Write the correct form of the word in capitals so that it collocates with all of the words and/or phrases in each group. There is an example at the beginning (**0**).

0 TIME	_timeless_	quality	appeal	classic
1 SUPPORT	_____	role	evidence	actor
2 maintain	lose your	regain your	_____	**COMPOSE**
3 competition	winning	dictionary	_____	**ENTER**
4 cause considerable	suffer great	overcome economic	_____	**HARD**
5 show proof of	reveal someone's	a case of mistaken	_____	**IDENTIFY**

2 Complete the sentences with one of the collocations from exercise **1**. You may need to change some of the words. There is an example at the beginning (**0**).

0 Many of Disney's early films are ____timeless classics____, which continue to be enjoyed even now in the modern computer age.

1 A photograph of the _____ in this year's Inventor of the Future competition will be printed in the April edition of _Science Today_ magazine.

2 At the age of 82, Christopher Plummer won the Oscar for Best _____ for his role in the film _Beginners_.

3 Joseph Rendell was arrested in what seems to have been _____ ; police are still looking for a Joseph Randall in connection with the robbery.

4 He was visibly shocked at the news; it was a while before he _____ and was calm enough to ask how it had happened.

5 The dramatic increase in house prices and rents has _____ to those on low incomes.

Language focus

 Grammar reference on page 222 of the Coursebook.

Creating emphasis

In each of the following sentences there is a word which should not be there. Cross out the word. There is an example at the beginning (**0**).

0 What annoys me so much about her is the fact ~~of~~ that she never helps with the washing up.

1 It was just after we arrived at the hotel that we have received a call from our neighbour telling us we'd been burgled.

2 I used to hate going to visit my grandparents: all what we ever did was watch television and listen to my granddad talking about politics.

3 It might have been because Jane that rang when I was in the shower – she's the only person I know who'd phone so early in the day.

4 It's not so much what she says that annoys me, and it's more the way she says it.

5 He realized he had little hope of finding his way out of the forest in the fog, so what he did it was to build himself a shelter out of branches and leaves.

6 It was only when the police came at three o'clock in the morning so that they finally turned their music down.

Multiple-choice cloze

For questions **1–8**, read the text below and then decide which answer (**A**, **B**, **C** or **D**) best fits each gap. There is an example at the beginning (**0**).

Lost luggage

You get off your plane and (**0**) .... your way to the baggage reclaim area. After quite some time spent waiting, there is no (**1**) .... of your bags and you begin to consider the possibility that they may have gone (**2**) .... What should you do?

Firstly, don't panic. The most likely (**3**) .... is that your bags simply didn't make it onto the flight, perhaps because they were mislaid at the departure airport, or perhaps because the aircraft had already (**4**) .... its weight allowance. If they (**5**) .... to appear on the carousel, report the loss before you leave the baggage hall and go through customs.

Recovering your luggage should be no problem, provided you've kept (**6**) .... of your baggage checks – those little barcodes stuck to the back of your tickets at check-in.

Go to the handling agent's desk and (**7**) .... a Property Irregularity Report (PIR) form, which describes the checked bag and its contents. Then, ask the baggage-services manager for a contact telephone number and confirm that your bags will be forwarded to your final (**8**) ....

0 A go	**B** get	**C** make	**D** walk
1 A indication	**B** sign	**C** notice	**D** mark
2 A lost	**B** missing	**C** absent	**D** misplaced
3 A example	**B** understanding	**C** clarification	**D** explanation
4 A surpassed	**B** overtaken	**C** exceeded	**D** outdone
5 A lack	**B** omit	**C** avoid	**D** fail
6 A control	**B** hold	**C** property	**D** hand
7 A carry out	**B** complete	**C** fulfil	**D** realize
8 A destination	**B** destiny	**C** termination	**D** terminus

Open cloze

For questions **1–8**, read the text below and think of the word which best fits each gap. Use only **one** word in each gap. There is an example at the beginning (**0**).

Write your answers **IN CAPITAL LETTERS**.

The revolution in the way we travel

Not so long (**0**) ..*AGO*.. , it was only mainstream travel agencies that had the technology to search airline and hotel reservations systems. Many were (**1**) .... more than order-takers but enjoyed a ten per cent commission on package tours. But (**2**) .... days have gone. Travel and the Internet are made (**3**) .... one another, connecting a global inventory of seats and beds with millions of travellers. The future for these agencies looks bleak, (**4**) .... they begin to add value by offering real expertise. (**5**) .... recruiting experienced agents who (**6**) .... themselves had personal experience of overseas destinations, and equipping them with the technology necessary for telephone sales, they can offer customers a professional service (**7**) .... the comfort of their own home. Catering for a new market of people that have not been near a travel agency (**8**) .... they first acquired a broadband connection may be the only way to survive for tour operators.

Word formation

For questions **1–8**, read the text below. Use the word given in capitals at the end of some of the lines to form a word that fits in the gap **in the same line**. There is an example at the beginning **(0)**.

Write your answers **IN CAPITAL LETTERS**.

Women only

(0) _INCREASINGLY_ , women are taking their holidays without men. **INCREASE**
For **(1)** .... reasons, camaraderie or just plain fun, a growing **SAFE**
number of female tourists are signing up for women-only trips.
Twenty-five years or so ago, only a **(2)** .... of companies offered **HAND**
such holidays; now there are several hundred. Travel **(3)** .... **CONSULT**
Jo Littlewood says that the combination of higher incomes with delayed
marriage, divorce, retirement and widowhood has **(4)** .... more **ABLE**
women to travel, often on their own. They are attracted by the sense of
freedom that a holiday without men affords them. 'Women in a group
tend to feel **(5)** .... and speak more openly than when men are **INHIBIT**
around,' she adds. 'It's also a lot more fun. Women laugh a lot more
(6) .... than men, probably because they don't mind laughing **READY**
at themselves.' Jill Cummings is a regular traveler with Everywoman Tours,
an Oxford-based company whose very name is a **(7)** .... to **DETER**
men. 'And a good thing too.' She says. 'Men simply cannot resist the
(8) .... to try and take control, wherever they are. Thankfully, **TEMPT**
there is none of that with Everywoman.'

Key word transformation

For questions **1–6**, complete the second sentence so that it has a similar meaning to
the first sentence, using the word given. **Do not change the word given.** You must
use between **three** and **six** words, including the word given. There is an example at the
beginning **(0)**.

Write your answers **IN CAPITAL LETTERS**.

0 Immediately after Emi quit her job, she booked a package tour around Europe.

HAD

As ....*SOON AS SHE HAD HANDED*.......... in her notice Emi booked a package tour around
Europe.

1 I didn't stop worrying about the wild animals until we were safe inside camp.

ONLY

It was .... safety of camp that I stopped worrying about
the wild animals.

2 Steve's one topic of conversation is the time he spent as a pilot.

EVER

The time he spent as a pilot .... about.

3 After arriving at the airport, we realized that our passports were still at home.

UNTIL

It .... at the airport that we realized our passports were
still at home.

4 I first noticed the backpacker while I was looking at some brochures.

LOOK

It was .... at some brochures that I first noticed the
backpacker.

5 When we got to the resort we discovered that it was better than we expected.

TURNED

When we got to the resort .... be better than we
expected.

6 They began calmly discussing football but soon started arguing fiercely about politics.

HEATED

What began as a calm discussion about football soon developed
.... about politics.

Report

1 Read the following Writing Part 2 task. Before you write your answer, do the related
planning and vocabulary tasks in exercises **2–3** below.

You have been asked to write a report for your national tourism authority about tourist
attractions in your country. Your report should

- explain why two tourist attractions are popular.
- outline some problems associated with these sites.
- suggest ways of improving the attractions.

Write your **report** in **220–260** words.

2 Decide whether the statements **1–5** about writing this report are true (T) or false (F).

Content

1 It's acceptable to write about more than two attractions if you prefer.

Organization and cohesion

2 Either of the two plans on page 75 would be acceptable.

Plan A

Introduction

Explanations – attractions 1 and 2

Problem(s) – attractions 1 and 2

Suggestions for improvements

Plan B

Introduction

Explanation and problem(s) – attraction 1

Explanation and problem(s) – attraction 2

Suggestions for improvements

3 An overall heading and individual paragraph headings are completely unnecessary.

Range of language

4 A range of descriptive language would be useful here.

Target reader and register

5 An informal and chatty register would be best in this context.

Vocabulary development: Collocations

3 For **1–5**, cross out the word in *italics* which does **not** collocate with the word(s) in **bold**.

1 This has led to *urban/poor/serious/widespread/localized* **congestion.**

2 Tickets are *unacceptably/highly/competitively/likely/attractively* **priced**.

3 It suffers from a/an *ineffective/unqualified/misleading/confusing/ill-considered* **advertising campaign**.

4 There is/are *run down/inadequate/ample/a shortage of/destructive* **facilities**

5 **Information** about the site is *prosperous/unremarkable/illuminating/engaging/detailed*.

4 Now write your **report** in **220–260** words.

Reading and
Use of English
Part 5

Multiple choice

You are going to read a magazine article about young people who have chosen to live with their parents again. For questions **1–6**, choose the answer (**A**, **B**, **C** or **D**) which you think fits best according to the text.

Back to the nest

Spiralling property prices and the collapse of the labour market are forcing many young people (and some not so young) to move back in with their parents. But how are both generations coping with this living arrangement?

When stand-up comedian Nat Luurtsema hit the ripe old age of 28, she found herself living back in her parents' house in the Hertfordshire town of Watford. For six long months she languished amid the boy-band posters of her childhood bedroom, and traipsed round, like a reluctant toddler, after her mum in the supermarket. 'When I moved back I really felt I had messed up,' she says. 'I was so lonely I started blogging about it. That turned out to be my saving grace. Loads of people started getting in touch saying they were in the same position; I even had emails from high-flying corporate managers saying they were back with mum. The response was amazing. I stumbled upon a zeitgeist.' Luurtsema, it soon became clear, was part of a 'boomerang generation' – the group of young adults who have found themselves returning to the family nest.

There is something of a preoccupation with the living arrangements of these boomerangers right now. Currently one of the biggest shows in the States is *Girls*, written by 25-year-old Lena Dunham, about four twentysomethings adrift in a sea of unpaid internships and sofa-surfing in New York. Dunham, incidentally, wrote most of it while living at home with her own mum and dad. Then there's the cumbersomely titled *How to Live with your Parents for the Rest of your Life* – an entire sitcom built around the premise – which is currently being piloted on the ABC network. It's not surprising, then, that Luurtsema's blog was swiftly picked up by publishing company Hodder and turned into a book, entitled *Cuckoo in the Nest*. The figures speak for themselves. A US report published last month found that as many as three in ten are returning to the family nest – the highest proportion since the 1950s.

According to parenting expert Sue Atkins, the nature of the experience is dictated by how well a new set of boundaries is established. 'Given the chance, these young adults will revert back to being teenagers again,' she claims. In order to stop any regression, Atkins proposes that parents say 'This is a new phase of your life now and it's going to be different.' 'They have to sit down and have a conversation about them paying their way and what is acceptable and what is not. Then follow up on it and make sure they're not taken for a ride.'

It's interesting that, whatever the circumstances, everyone Nat talked to had a firm moving out date set – usually within a year-and-a-half – both for their own sanity and to avoid imposing on their parents. For Luurtsema, it was around the six-month mark that she knew her time in Watford had to come to an end. There's a moment in the book that says it all: she had just finished a gig and was hanging out backstage with comedians Richard Herring and Stephen Merchant when, absent-mindedly, she pulled from her bag a Tupperware box containing a packed lunch made by her mum. 'A heavy silence broke out, with undertones of pity,' she writes. Shortly after, she was gone.

Actress Gemma Swead, 27, moved back in with her parents after she'd been working in Los Angeles for three years. Having now been with them for a year and a half, she says 'There was no question about me going back. In fact, it was just kind of assumed I would. I am very, very close to both parents.' She concedes, however, that 'the fact that they want to know everything – not in a controlling way – means they can get a little bit on top of me. If I'm down, they will want to know if everything is all right. And they repeat things just to make sure I've heard. So now, if one of them asks me the same question more than once I just pretend I didn't hear it. But at the same time I wouldn't change any of it. Right now I am totally focused on my career. I wouldn't be able to do what I'm trying to do without them.'

It does make you wonder what impact this might have in the future. Are we heading for

an era where adolescence stretches right through the twenties? Are these 'kids' going to be holding down jobs while still getting their shirts washed and meals cooked? Or will it create a new, modern family structure with stronger, more adult bonds between generations and a chance for some of your parents' terrible memories of you as a stroppy teen to be extinguished?

1 When Nat Luurtsema began to blog about her experience of living at home, she
   A felt humiliated by some of the comments she received.
   B was relieved to discover that others were in a similar position.
   C was surprised to be contacted by people she knew from work.
   D felt reluctant about revealing all her personal details.

2 What does the writer suggest about Nat's Luurtsema's book in the second paragraph?
   A The story it tells is more convincing than others on the same theme.
   B The US public may be unreceptive to a British writer's experience.
   C There are elements of it which come across as slightly clichéd.
   D Its subject matter seems to be growing in popularity at the moment.

3 Parenting expert Sue Atkins maintains that adults who move back in with their parents
   A tend to
   B need to
   C have to
   D must re

4 The writer _____ in order to
   A make t _____ for granted.
   B show h _____ s can vary.
   C suppor _____ ts must be limited.
   D illustra _____ e parental home.

5 What are _____
   A She car _____ ress their concern.
   B She res _____ r personal freedom.
   C She int _____ w employment.
   D She had never expected to live with her parents again once she had left home.

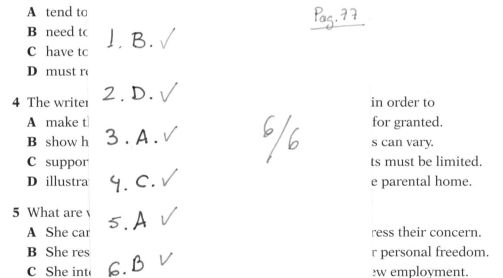

Pag. 77

1. B. ✓

2. D. ✓

3. A. ✓

4. C. ✓

5. A ✓

6. B ✓

6/6

6 The writer suggests that living arrangements in the future may mean that
   A the next generation of adults has no sense of responsibility.
   B the relationship between parents and adult children improves.
   C the significance of the parental role will eventually diminish.
   D adults will choose to delay having children of their own.

Vocabulary

Wordlist on page 213 of the Coursebook.

1 In **A** and **B** complete the sentences with one of the words from the boxes.

A

> bee   dog   owl   lion   mouse

1 I was woken up at two o'clock by an inconsiderate _____ **hooting** monotonously in the tree next to my tent.

2 We heard the **squeaking** of a _____ coming from the cupboard where we had set the trap.

3 A honey _____ came **buzzing** past, a sign that spring had at last arrived.

4 The neighbours' _____ spends the day **whining** and scratching at the door while they're both out at work.

5 What's the name of the company that has that _____ **roaring** before the beginning of each film?

B

> leaves   floorboards   stomach   drum   music

1 His _____ **rumbled**, reminding him that he hadn't eaten since lunchtime.

2 The _____ **rustled** in the gentle breeze.

3 I wish that child would stop **banging** that _____ !

4 You can't complain – you have your _____ **blaring out** all day.

5 We heard voices and the sound of footsteps on **creaking** _____ .

2 Choose the correct answer **A**, **B**, **C** or **D**.

1 He's a very well-behaved little boy – I rarely have to _____ my voice to him.
   A shout   **B** lose   **C** raise   **D** lift

2 As we climbed higher, the noise of the traffic gradually _____ away.
   A faded   **B** left   **C** grew   **D** weakened

3 I couldn't hear what they were saying; they were in the next room so their voices were _____ .
   A booming   **B** muffled   **C** hoarse   **D** rough

4 She came in, picked up her things, and left before I could _____ a sound.
   A pronounce   **B** tell   **C** express   **D** utter

5 There was a _____ party going on next door last night; the police eventually came at half past one and put a stop to it.
   A constant   **B** continuous   **C** roomy   **D** rowdy

6 He proposed to her in the _____ lit restaurant of the hotel with piano music playing in the background.
   A soundly   **B** softly   **C** smoothly   **D** sparsely

7 Cleaners worked overtime to get the place looking spick and _____ for the presidential visit.
   A spam   **B** spot   **C** spin   **D** span

8 Factory workers lived in council flats which were _____ built and badly maintained.
   A poorly   **B** weakly   **C** highly   **D** slightly

9 Immigrants live in _____ conditions, with up to 15 sharing a small room.
   A spacious   **B** cramped   **C** restrained   **D** constrained

10 The town is ideally _____ for visiting both London and the south coast.
   A set   **B** centred   **C** orientated   **D** situated

Language focus

 Grammar reference on page 222 of the Coursebook.

Participle clauses

Combine the following pairs of sentences using participle clauses.

Examples:

Sheffield FC was founded in 1857. This makes it the oldest football club in the world.

Sheffield FC was founded in 1857, making it the oldest football club in the world.

He inherited a huge sum of money from his grandmother. He decided to give up work.

Having inherited a huge sum of money from his grandmother, he decided to give up work.

1 *Lord of the Rings: Return of the King* won 11 Oscars. It equalled the record held by *Ben Hur* and *Titanic* for the highest number of Academy Awards.

2 We finally discovered where the leak was. We called in a plumber.

3 The school now has 1254 students. This represents a 6 per cent increase on last year's figure.

4 Part of the stadium roof collapsed. It injured six spectators.

5 I am not a parent. I can take my holidays whenever I like.

6 The team has had a disastrous season so far. It has won only three of its last sixteen games.

7 Our parents went away for the weekend. My brother and I had a party.

8 I was walking home from school yesterday. I bumped into Alex.

Open cloze

Reading and Use of English
Part 2

For questions **1–8**, read the text below and think of the word which best fits each gap. Use only **one** word in each gap. There is an example at the beginning (**0**).

Write your answers **IN CAPITAL LETTERS**.

High-rise buildings

Plans for high-rise buildings in London and Liverpool are being contested as opposition grows (**0**) ....*TO*.... the tall, the ostentatious, and the 'iconic'. The people opposing the new towers are (**1**) .... necessarily traditional conservatives and architectural purists, but young activists and many people usually associated (**2**) .... the avant-garde. In (**3**) .... sense, these buildings are seen as out of time, (**4**) .... been conceived in the last economic boom but built during a recession – and in another, as out of place, particularly in four-storey streetscapes. Part of the wider problem is that (**5**) .... in the past tower blocks were built with the poor (**6**) .... mind, these buildings are mostly for the luxury market, aiming to attract investment money from overseas, (**7**) .... is why opponents view them as socially divisive. Estate agent Nigel Abbot disagrees: 'Taller buildings maximize available space in congested cities. It's (**8**) .... wonder that there are plans to build into the sky.'

Multiple-choice cloze

For questions **1–8**, read the text below and decide which answer (**A**, **B**, **C** or **D**) best fits each gap. There is an example at the beginning (**0**).

Flat to let

Location: Norfolk Gardens, Westgate

No. of bedrooms: 1

Price per week: £620

This large one-bedroomed flat, situated in the **(0)** .... residential suburb of Westgate and **(1)** .... St John's Park, is ideal for a busy single person or couple. The accommodation is **(2)** .... located in the heart of the suburb within easy walking distance of the wide range of amenities offered by both Westgate and the fashionable Donatello Road Market.

Newly decorated and carpeted, the property **(3)** .... a double bedroom, good-sized reception room, large living room, fully fitted kitchen and a bathroom with quality shower. Tenants also have **(4)** .... of their own secure underground parking space. The flat is simply but **(5)** .... furnished and the south-facing living room is pleasantly light and **(6)** .... , with large picture windows which offer superb views of the surrounding area.

What **(7)** .... this property apart from other accommodation with similar **(8)** .... is its very acceptable price, given its central location and excellent transport links to other parts of the city. For further details or to arrange a viewing telephone 020 786 50990.

0	**A** greenish	**B** <u>leafy</u>	**C** flowering	**D** blooming
1	**A** overseeing	**B** overhanging	**C** overlooking	**D** overreaching
2	**A** appropriately	**B** fittingly	**C** suitably	**D** conveniently
3	**A** composes	**B** comprises	**C** comprehends	**D** compounds
4	**A** service	**B** employment	**C** application	**D** use
5	**A** sparsely	**B** plainly	**C** richly	**D** tastefully
6	**A** draughty	**B** breezy	**C** airy	**D** gusty
7	**A** sets	**B** puts	**C** keeps	**D** holds
8	**A** types	**B** kinds	**C** characteristics	**D** aspects

Reading and
Use of English
Part 3

Word formation

For questions **1–8** read the text below. Use the word given in capitals at the end of some of the lines to form a word that fits in the gap **in the same line**. There is an example at the beginning **(0)**. Write your answers **IN CAPITAL LETTERS**.

Treehouses

In some of Britain's most exclusive **(0)** ....NEIGHBOURHOODS.... where **NEIGHBOUR**
swimming pools and conservatories are commonplace, the most
stylish are opting for the only addition **(1)** .... to turn the **GUARANTEE**
neighbours green – a luxury treehouse for adults. **(2)** .... more **COST**
than £20 000, they come with drinks cabinets, dining tables,
(3) .... kitchens and balconies. Some owners find their treehouses **FIT**
are perfect for holding **(4)** .... business meetings, and one **INTERRUPT**
businessman liked his so much that he made it into a permanent office.

Derek and Edwina Lilley spent £24 000 on Britain's most **(5)** .... **LUXURY**
and extravagant treehouse. It took four weeks to build and can
accommodate 35 for drinks parties with ease. It has a kitchen
(6) .... with a combination oven, grill and hob, as well as hot and **EQUIP**
cold **(7)** .... water. The upper-crust treehouses are the product of **RUN**
a Scottish company called Peartree, which built 50 in its first year.
Planning **(8)** .... is not needed as they are regarded as **PERMIT**
temporary buildings.

Reading and
Use of English
Part 4

Key word transformation

For questions **1–6**, complete the second sentence so that it has a similar meaning to the first sentence, using the word given. **Do not change the word given**. You must use between **three** and **six** words, including the word given. There is an example at the beginning **(0)**. Write your answers **IN CAPITAL LETTERS**.

0 The police asked Mr Porter many questions about exactly where he was on the night of his wife's murder.

RELATION

The police asked Mr Porter many questions ____*IN RELATION TO HIS EXACT*____
whereabouts on the night of his wife's murder.

1 As I didn't want to disappoint my parents, I agreed to go to medical school.

LET

Not _____ my parents, I agreed to go to medical school.

2 After deciding he would leave home, Enrique immediately began searching for an apartment.

DECISION

Having _____ leave home, Enrique immediately began searching for an apartment.

3 Make sure you look after your bag in this café as there are many thieves around.

EYE

I'd advise you _____ your bag in this café as there are many thieves around.

4 I feel certain that there will be a new government after the election.

BOUND

In my opinion, there_____ of government after the election.

5 No-one in my department admitted that the mistake was their fault.

RESPONSIBILITY

No-one in my department was willing _____ the mistake.

6 Someone has made the suggestion that our current data-entry system be replaced.

RID

It has been _____ our current data-entry system.

Essay

1 Read the following Writing Part 1 task and the model answer below. Does the model answer respond to **all** parts of the question?

Your class has attended a seminar on what methods governments could use to help young people find suitable accommodation. You have made the notes below:

> **Methods governments could use to help young people find suitable accommodation.**
>
> • building programme
> • market regulation
> • financial assistance

> Some opinions expressed in the seminar:
> 'We need more low-cost housing.'
> 'Laws should be introduced to minimize rents.'
> 'Young people living with their parents should receive help from the government.'

Write an essay discussing **two** of the methods in your notes. You should **explain which method you think is more important** for governments to consider, **giving reasons** in support of your answer.

You may, if you wish, make use of the opinions expressed in the seminar, but you should use your own words as far as possible.

Model answer

In recent years many young people have found it increasingly difficult to find accommodation that meets their needs. The options available are either prohibitively expensive, very poor quality, far from their place of work or study, or some combination of these factors. Placing additional pressure on young people as they try to continue their education or enter the workforce is an unfortunate consequence of this situation.

One possible solution is to encourage young people to live at home with their parents for longer. Creating a financial incentive, such as a government grant, might motivate more young people to choose this option. However, while initially an attractive proposition, the reality is that many young people are already compelled to stay at home for want of any alternative and as a result their opportunities to work or study in a different city are severely restricted.

Perhaps a more appropriate strategy would be to construct a range of affordable housing near the city centre. This might take the form of simple but comfortable apartment complexes built on vacant lots, which are available in many cities. In this way the authorities could both create employment and bring fresh life to what are sometimes run-down areas. The finished apartments would subsequently provide modestly priced accommodation for young people, located close to colleges and workplaces.

An initiative of this type would generate opportunities and benefits for the wider society, while failing to act would only see the effects of the current housing shortage made worse. For these reasons the government should be encouraged to take decisive action.

2 Underline the words and phrases in the model answer which give the reason for/result of a course of action.

Example: an unfortunate consequence of

Vocabulary development: Expressing opinions

3 Complete the sentences with a past participle from the box. There is an example at the beginning (0).

applauded   condemned   confirmed   ignored   forgotten   misrepresented   ~~recognized~~

0 The effects of this practice are now widely __*recognized*__ as being harmful to people's health.

1 It was always suspected that there was shortage of affordable housing. Now studies have _____ this beyond doubt.

2 The evidence is now so overwhelming that it cannot be _____ ; the government must take immediate action.

3 The debate, which raged for many weeks last year, is all but _____ now; the media clearly have a very short memory.

4 The facts have been _____; the company's vested interest in the outcome of the enquiry has led them to be rather economical with the truth.

5 The council's actions are being _____ by all parties and quite rightly so in my opinion. There is simply no excuse for such poor judgement.

6 It's one of the best exhibitions I've seen in years. The gallery should be _____ for managing to bring so much of his work to the city.

4 Look at the following Writing Part 1 task.

Methods the college should use to help students find suitable accommodation

- lower rent
- better assistance
- more flexibility

Some opinions expressed in the workshop:

'Staying in college halls of residence should be cheaper.'

'The college should provide a service that helps students find accommodation.'

'Halls of residence close over summer but some students have nowhere else to go.'

Your class has attended a workshop on what methods your college should use to help students find suitable accommodation. You have made the notes below.

Write an essay discussing **two** of the methods in your notes. You should **explain which method you think is more important** for the college to consider, **giving reasons** in support of your answer.

You may, if you wish, make use of the opinions expressed in the discussion, but you should use your own words as far as possible.

Now write your answer in **220–260** words.

Multiple matching

1 You are going to read an article about the influence of classical music on children. For questions **1–10**, choose from the sections **A–E**. The sections may be chosen more than once.

In which section are the following mentioned?

a positive comparison between two examples of classical music	**1**
an obstacle that a project is still trying to overcome	**2**
the impression that music had been created in order to complement the spoken word	**3**
the sense of anticipation common to a group of children	**4**
a contrast between the effects of two musical genres on young children	**5**
a commonly held negative perception about the nature of classical music	**6**
influences on the direction that the writer's career took	**7**
an experience far exceeding the writer's expectations of it	**8**
exposure to classical music being part of the childhood experience	**9**
the suggestion that children need a visual aspect to be attracted to classical music	**10**

Wider horizons

Rory Bremner explains how listening to the child-friendly Peter and the Wolf *made him a classical music fan for life*

A

How many of us can remember our first encounter with classical music? It may have been a recital, a trip to the theatre or concert hall – or listening to the records or radio
5 programmes that were part of your early family life, gradually assimilated as they played in the background. I can't remember a specific occasion, but I do remember the bizarre and random record collection
10 my brother and I somehow accumulated as children: the comedy duo Flanders and Swann and the Monty Python sketches we listened to testified to a love of comedy, a delight in wordplay and voices that were
15 clearly the inspiration behind my eventual becoming a comedian. There was also a Disney recording of Russian composer Prokofiev's *Peter and the Wolf*.

B

And so it was that I was drawn by that
20 story into the world of the orchestra as the narrator, Sterling Holloway, introduced the instruments as characters — the clarinet

as Ivan the cat, the oboe as Sonia the duck, the string section as Peter and so
25 on. To my mind the work ranks alongside Saint-Saëns' *Carnival of the Animals* with its elephant, tortoises and the sublime swan, as one of the great introductions to classical music. Almost 30 years later I was
30 sitting on stage in an Oxford concert hall, waiting to narrate a performance of *Peter and the Wolf*. The audience filed in: parents leading their little ones, some shy and even apprehensive, having never (I imagined)
35 seen a full orchestra before. I remember being profoundly moved by the excitement and wonder in that room; the thought that, for some of these young minds, the experience might be the first discovery of the
40 possibilities of music, the planting of a seed, the wakening of an imagination. It seems extraordinary that *Peter and the Wolf* was written as long ago as 1936, the *Carnival of the Animals* 50 years earlier. So isn't it about
45 time that someone created some modern, funny stories to get children listening to classical music?

C

And now someone has done something about it, a music teacher named Matt Parry, who
50 has woven an original story around Rimsky-Korsakov's music for *Scheherazade*. The project has started life as a CD recording, but has the potential to be a lot more: a musical app, an interactive website, an animated
55 film, a live show. Parry is evangelical in his belief that classical music has the potential to develop children's imaginations and their ability to listen and absorb quite complicated 'information' in a way that pop music simply
60 doesn't. This is something they'll benefit from for the rest of their lives. And the spark is undeniably there – after all, children enjoy the mock classical scores of the *Harry Potter*, *Star Wars* and *Batman* films, so it's just a case
65 of presenting music in the right way, with stories and powerful imagery, to get them hooked on it.

D

And so it was that I found myself in an unprepossessing recording studio near
70 Hampton Court. Having turned up for what I imagined would be a straightforward piece of voiceover, (my job was simply to add a voice for Sinbad, the Chief Pirate), I was blown

away by the ambition and enchantment of
75 what Parry was creating, with its playfulness and enthusiasm and the quite remarkable way in which he had made the dialogue fit the music: as if they were meant to be together, the music written to accompany
80 the script, rather than the other way round. Parry's new production sweeps away all the 'stuffiness' and over-formality that is often associated with classical music. And all of this created with a fellow music teacher, with
85 an orchestra drawn from his friends and the help of some talented musical actors.

E

EMI Classics showed interest in the project, but things stalled following EMI's takeover by Universal Music last year. Undaunted,
90 Parry has now launched a campaign through the crowd funding organization Kickstarter, through which supporters of his project can buy the CD and pre-order a graphic novel to accompany it. It's an idea that deserves to
95 take off, bringing children to classical music much as the children's book series *Horrible Histories* got them learning about history. I'm just excited to be part of it and hope that one day soon, a child like the one I once was will
100 come across *Scheherazade*, and be inspired.

2 a In **1–8** below, complete each gap with one word so that the second sentence has the same meaning as the first. The answer to the second sentence is taken from the reading text on pages 84–85. There is an example at the beginning **(0)**. Do the exercise without looking at the reading text on pages 84–85.

0 I well remember the first time I met this band.

I have a vivid memory of **my first** ____*encounter*____ **with** this band. (1–2)

1 When I wrote this book, it was a visit to Prague that influenced me.

My visit to Prague **was the** _____ **behind** this book. (14–15)

2 This small, low-budget film deserves just as much recognition as any Hollywood epic on the subject of war.

This small, low-budget film **ranks** _____ any Hollywood epic **as one of** the great war movies. (25–28)

3 This experience will be useful to you for the rest of your life.

It's an experience that **you'll** _____ **from** for the rest of your life! (60)

4 Many young readers became addicted to the *Harry Potter* novels because of the wonderful characters.

It was the wonderful characters that **got** many young readers _____ **on** the *Harry Potter* novels. (66–67)

5 The sheer size of the sculpture really impressed me.

I **was** _____ **away by** the sheer size of the sculpture. (73–74)

6 There is a commonly held perception that opera is only for the wealthy.

Opera **is often** _____ **with** the wealthy. (82–83)

7 The publishers said they thought the book had potential.

The publishers **showed** _____ **in** the book. (87)

8 It's a great project so success would be justified.

It's a great project that deserves **to** _____ **off**. (94–95)

b Check your answers in the reading text on pages 84–85. The relevant line numbers are given in brackets.

Vocabulary

Wordlist on page 213 of the Coursebook.

A Sight

Underline the correct alternative.

1 Icy roads and **poor** *visibility/sight/view* due to fog meant driving conditions were extremely dangerous.

2 I've always **had poor** *eyesight/view/look*, whereas my brother, who's 56, still **has twenty-twenty** *vision/eye/sight* and will probably never have to wear glasses.

3 I'd hate to be a film star, always **in the public** *vision/eye/show*, recognized wherever you go.

4 As soon as I mentioned Sally, Paul **gave me a knowing** *sight/view/look*. 'But Sally and I are just good friends,' I protested.

5 The cliffs were **a welcome** *vision/sight/show* after so many weeks at sea.

6 He suffered a heart attack on stage, **in** *complete/open/full* **view of** the audience.

7 I picked up the shiny stone to **take a** *handier/tighter/closer* look.

8 For most of this week the comet will be **visible with the** *naked/bare/open* **eye**.

9 Could you *keep/put/set* **your eye on** my bag, please? I'm just going to the toilet.

10 We scanned the night sky, hoping to *give/catch/gain* **sight of** the comet.

B Read and write

1 Complete the phrasal verbs with an appropriate word from the box. In each section **1–4** the word required for both spaces is the same.

> up   into   off   out

1 I've just **written** _____ **to** the Polish Tourist Office for information on the Masurian Lakes.

Western governments have come under increasing pressure to **write** _____ Third World debts.

2 As soon as the interview was over, he **wrote** _____ **his notes** and emailed the report to his boss.

Contract law is a complex area, so it's wise to **read** _____ **on the subject** and take professional advice.

3 She swallowed hard and **wrote** _____ **a cheque for** £4560.

Let's hear what you've written for number 3. Can you **read** _____ **your answer**, please, Alex?

4 The right to keep and bear arms is **written** _____ **the constitution** of the United States.

It's only an opinion poll – it would be wrong to **read too much** _____ **the results**.

2 Match each pair of definitions **a–d** to the appropriate pair of verbs in **bold** in exercise **1** above.
a include in (a law, contract or agreement); think something means more than it really does

b record in a full and complete form; read a lot about a subject in order to get information

c apply to an organization asking them to send something; cancel

d complete a printed document (e.g. prescription, receipt) with information; read aloud

Language focus

(G) Grammar reference on pages 222–223 of the Coursebook.

Inversion

1 Complete each of the gaps with one word.

Statement from the main opposition party

At **(1)** _____ time in the last 60 years **(2)** _____ literacy levels in this country been so low. Not only **(3)** _____ the nation's teenagers reading less than ever before, **(4)** _____ many are also incapable of writing more than one sentence without making a spelling or punctuation mistake. **(5)** _____ since the 1940s have we witnessed such a decline in reading and writing standards.

(6) _____ no circumstances must this situation be permitted to continue. Only **(7)** _____ the government introduces a comprehensive reading programme for three to five-year-olds **(8)** _____ standards improve. **(9)** _____ then will the nation's youth be able to break free from the chains of illiteracy and recover its dignity. **(10)** _____ no account must we allow ourselves to be complacent; action must be taken now.

---

2 Complete the sentences with a suitable phrase. There is an example at the beginning (0).

0 Not for one moment _____*did we suspect*_____ that David had stolen it – it took us all completely by surprise.

1 No sooner _____ home than my mother phoned.

2 Only when _____ the news on television did she realize the full scale of the tragedy.

3 Never before in all my working life _____ such an incompetent boss.

4 Not until you've tidied your room _____ you to go out and play with your friends!

5 Hardly _____ his new job when the company ran into problems and made him redundant.

6 At no point in the marathon _____ of giving up: I had promised myself I would finish it.

7 Never again _____ her advice – I'm in more trouble now than I was before.

8 Little _____ that someone was recording their conversation.

Reading and Use of English
Part 1

Multiple-choice cloze

For questions **1–8**, read the text below and decide which answer (**A**, **B**, **C** or **D**) best fits each gap. There is an example at the beginning (**0**).

Opera for everyone

You could be forgiven for **(0)** ...... the Royal Opera House (ROH) more with the over-50s than with the under-15s. But if you did, then you might be surprised to learn that the ROH's education department reaches out every year to **(1)** ...... the young generation with opera. It is, however, safe to assume that opera can be an unfamiliar **(2)** ...... to most schoolchildren, and the first reaction **(3)** ...... by the ROH in the classroom is often bemusement. 'Children **(4)** ...... positively as long as you introduce them to opera in the right way,' explains Paul Reeve, the ROH's director of education. 'The older students can initially have an extreme negative reaction, but that **(5)** ...... is a great challenge. We give those **(6)** ...... kids the opportunity to experience what it's like to be, say, a composer or a choreographer, and that shows them the skill that is **(7)** ...... in the art forms.' One popular programme the ROH **(8)** ...... annually is 'Write an Opera' and this year children from 28 UK schools will perform their work on stage in July.

0 A tying	**B** relating	**C** joining	**D** <u>associating</u>
1 A reveal	**B** keep	**C** engage	**D** maintain
2 A way	**B** medium	**C** channel	**D** means
3 A developed	**B** projected	**C** provided	**D** encountered
4 A respond	**B** manage	**C** answer	**D** learn
5 A refusal	**B** resistance	**C** indifference	**D** disillusionment
6 A ironic	**B** doubtful	**C** sceptical	**D** improbable
7 A requested	**B** contained	**C** involved	**D** included
8 A sets up	**B** runs up	**C** comes up	**D** takes up

Word formation

For questions **1–8**, read the text below. Use the word given in capitals at the end of some of the lines to form a word that fits in the gap **in the same line**. There is an example at the beginning **(0)**.

Write your answers **IN CAPITAL LETTERS**.

A COUNTRY AND WESTERN DEGREE

Lyrics from country and western songs have **(0)** <u>ENABLED</u> a student	**ABLE**
to obtain a degree in geography and **(1)** .... management.	**ENVIRONMENT**
Sally Hill, who **(2)** .... in cultural and social geography during	**SPECIAL**
her three-year course, analysed in **(3)** .... over 50 country songs	**DEEP**
as part of a study of the changing nature of relationships. According to	
Sally, the lyrics provide a fascinating **(4)** .... into the way women's	**SIGHT**
(5) .... of men have evolved. From the 1970s she used material	**PERCEIVE**
by Tammy Wynette, including *Run Woman Run*, a song that was written	
from the point of view of an older woman **(6)** .... a younger	**ADVICE**
woman to return to the man she has left, as she 'may not find true love	
again'. From the 1990s she quotes Shania Twain, who, in *Man, I Feel*	
Like a Woman, **(7)** .... women to 'have a little fun' and 'go	**COURAGE**
totally crazy'. Sally says the inspiration for her idea came from her	
mother, a fan of country music who describes herself as 'a fiercely	
(8) .... and happily divorced woman'.	**DEPEND**

Key word transformation

Complete the second sentence so that it has a similar meaning to the first sentence, using the word given. **Do not change the word given**. You must use between **three** and **six** words, including the word given.

Write your answers **IN CAPITAL LETTERS**.

1 We saw a bear almost as soon as we began our journey.

   SIGHT

   No sooner had we set .... of a bear.

2 Although he had a poor upbringing, James has done well for himself.

   SPITE

   James has done well for himself, ... up in poverty.

3 We only realized what it was when we examined it more closely.

   LOOK

   Not until we took a .... realize what it was.

4 We found it surprising that so few came to the meeting.

   TURNOUT

   We did not expect there .... for the meeting.

5 Fame became too much for her and she became a recluse.

   EYE

   She could no longer put up .... and she became a recluse.

6 Check that your valuables cannot be seen by potential thieves.

   KEPT

   Make .... of sight of potential thieves.

Formal email

1 Read the following Writing Part 2 task and the model answer below. Would you be interested in taking part in a programme like this?

Your college is interested in setting up a student exchange programme with colleges abroad/in foreign countries. You have been asked by your college director to write an email that will be sent to a number of colleges in foreign countries to introduce the programme and assess potential interest.

Your email should:

- describe your college
- explain how the student exchange programme will work
- suggest how the programme would benefit both colleges.

Dear College Director,

I am writing on behalf of Heathbridge College, where I am a student leader. Heathbridge is a vibrant tertiary institution and a focal point for the local community. Over 3000 undergraduates are enrolled on a broad range of vocational and academic courses, **but** our particular emphasis is science and technology. We **also** offer exceptional facilities for arts, sporting and other recreational activities. Our latest initiative is the establishment of an international exchange programme, which your college might be interested in joining.

The preliminary proposal is for our students to transfer for a period of between one term and one year to a sister school overseas, **while** a contemporary from that college would move to Heathbridge. The two students would be studying related subjects and would have the option of taking up each other's accommodation, staying in a college hall or lodging with a host family. **However**, the latter two may incur additional expense.

Such a programme would be of enormous value to all concerned **because** we live in an increasingly globalized world. The experience of living in a foreign culture and gaining exposure to a different academic tradition would be a significant step in a student's personal development. **Furthermore**, the independence and sense of perspective gained by an exchange student might well prove to be an advantage in the process of job application and entering the workforce.

If you would like further details and to ascertain whether our two colleges are compatible, please do not hesitate to contact me.

Thank you for your attention.

Yours sincerely,

Jason Spencer

Write your **email** in **220–260** words.

Vocabulary development

2 In the writing paper it is important to use a wide range of vocabulary and structures relevant to the topic. Look at the model answer and underline all the nouns and noun phrases that relate to education.

Example: college

Cohesion

3 Look at the linking words and phrases highlighted in **bold** in the model answer. For each one decide which of the following words or phrases could replace it in the same place in the sentence. There may be more than one answer or no substitution may be possible.

1 but	however, on the other hand, although, despite
2 also	in addition, additionally, moreover, too, and
3 while	when, then, similarly, during, and at the same time
4 however	on the other hand, although, despite, but
5 because	as a result of, as, so, since, therefore
6 furthermore	too, in addition, and, what is more

Practice

4 Complete the sentences with one of the linking devices from the box. There may be more than one possible answer.

> so   despite   but   moreover   therefore   however   on the other hand
> furthermore   in addition   in spite of the fact that   while

1 Students taking part in the programme would benefit in many ways. _____, there would also be some costs involved.

2 At first I might find it difficult to live in a foreign country _____ I believe that I would learn a great deal from the experience.

3 _____ the programme might not appeal to everyone, I believe that there would still be widespread support from the students.

4 I have always wanted to study in a foreign country _____ I am delighted to have this opportunity.

5 I am certain that an exchange programme would be beneficial to both our colleges. I would _____ urge you to give the matter consideration.

6 I believe that the programme would help me academically. _____ , I am sure it would help me develop personally.

7 _____ Heathbridge is a small college, many students have expressed an interest in joining the programme.

8 _____ being separated from my friends and family, I believe it would be a rewarding experience.

5 Either: **a** write your own answer to the task in exercise **1** on page 90 or **b** answer the following question.

Your college has an exchange programme with a number of colleges in foreign countries. You wish to take part in the programme. You have filled in an application form and must also write a covering letter to your college director in support of your application.

Your covering letter should explain

• which college you would like to attend.

• how you will benefit from the programme.

• why you are the best candidate.

Now write your **letter** in **220–260** words.

Gapped text

1 You are going to read an extract from a magazine article about an attempt to film hippos. Six paragraphs have been removed from the extract. Choose from the paragraphs **A–G** the one that fits each gap **(1–6)**. There is one extra paragraph which you do not need to use.

Hippo Heaven

What happens to a hippo when it sinks beneath the surface? Mzima was the place to find out

If there's a 'must-see' for a freshwater naturalist in East Africa, then it's Mzima Spring in Kenya's Tsavo West National Park. I first became aware of it as a teenager, when I was enthralled by documentary makers Alan and Joan Root's classic film *Mzima: Portrait of a Spring* with its extraordinarily clear underwater images of hippos. Back then, I would have assumed that there were other sites like it, scattered throughout the continent.

1

I therefore counted myself fortunate when my partner Vicky and I eventually got the chance to visit Mzima itself with Alan Root. It was the dry season, and as Alan flew us over Tsavo I was looking forward to seeing Mzima for the first time. But when Alan dipped a wing, I was totally unprepared for what leapt out of the monochrome scorched plains.

2

I knew immediately that we had to make a film there and we believed that if we lived at Mzima for long enough then something incredible would reveal itself. Our goal was to film the behaviour of hippos under water to get some key sequences about which a story could be told. This meant diving with them so frequently that we gained their trust or filming them unobserved from an underwater hide.

3

So, after two weeks, we had only spent a total of thirty minutes underwater with no film and one attack to show for it. The chance of spending the thousands of hours underwater that we would normally do when making a film looked slim. Hippos are potentially more dangerous than crocodiles, but the more we explored the spring, the more numerous the crocodiles we found – and the bolder they became.

4

At the same time as trying to film underwater, we erected towers to give us an aerial view of the spring. From these, we could watch an entire group of hippos and look down through the water. What we saw was exciting. Female hippos were defending their young against crocodiles, but most extraordinary of all, we could see the hippos opening their mouths and having their teeth cleaned by Labeo fish, which swarmed inside their gaping jaws.

5

The first time I tried it, this latest hide was secreted in the shallows, in the shade of an overhanging fig tree. I was there waiting for the hippos to come close, when a troop of baboons arrived to investigate and discovered that the tree was in fruit. As they fled, figs started to rain down from above.

6

At first it wasn't too bad but then the baboons realized that the best figs were in the branches directly above me. All this eating made them thirsty so they descended for a drink before carrying on with the feast. By the time Vicky came to relieve me, this had been going on for several hours, and the hippos had fled. There was only one thing for it; we would have to set about filming remotely. We ended up with a camera fixed to the bed of the spring and it took nine more months for the hippos to get used to that!

A I knew only too well what was coming next, but I couldn't escape. The golden rule about hide work is always to have someone else with you when you get in and out; any disturbance is then associated with that person and not the hide. But on this occasion, I was alone.

B It rapidly became apparent to us that neither method was going to work. Whenever we tried to get into the water, the hippos would immediately either charge or flee. Meanwhile the local crocodiles became curious, and on the second or third dive on my way to the hide, I had been forced to fend one off by vigorously hitting it on the head with the camera.

C We were determined to film this underwater too, but progress was dismal. In an idea borrowed from Alan Root, our assistant constructed a new sort of hide, a type of 'reverse aquarium', comprising a large metal 'coffin', open on top, with a glass front through which we could film and stay dry.

D This may be because hippos can't see particularly well underwater. They compensate for this by being sensitive to sound, including the high-pitched sound produced by the camera. Despite our efforts, we couldn't muffle it.

E Nestled far beneath us was an oasis of liquid turquoise, set in a ring of yellow fever trees. We circled, and each time we passed over, we could see the forms of hippos asleep in the pool. Through the crystal clear water, we could make out the green shapes of crocodiles and pale blue fish.

F With this in mind, we decided to build a tunnel of protective steel mesh to access the hide more safely. As a solution it seemed obvious, but the hippos found it obvious, too, and moved away. We then left the hide alone for several months, hoping that the hippos would get used to it, but for some reason, they never did.

G However, when I was filming hippos elsewhere in East Africa for a documentary twenty years later, I discovered that this was not the case. The hippos were swimming in muddy water holes and coffee-coloured rivers, so no matter how exciting the behaviour visible above the surface, every time a hippo's nostrils pinched together, I knew my subject was about to disappear from view.

2 The following words are all used to describe water in the text:
> a **fresh**water naturalist   **crystal clear** water   **muddy** water holes

Complete the sentences below with an appropriate word from the box. The words are all collocates of water.

flood   rain   salt   tap   drinking   running   sparkling

1 A 'We'd like to drink water with our meal, please.'

   B 'Certainly, Madam. **Bottled** or _____ **water**?'

   A 'Bottled, please.'

   B 'And would you prefer **still** or _____ **water**?'

2 Don't fill your bottles up from that tap – it's not safe _____ **water**.

3 We collect _____ **water** in a large tank on the roof, then use it for things like watering the garden or cleaning the car.

4 The merganser is a species of duck which can be seen on either **fresh** or _____ **water**, depending on the time of year.

5 He lives in a house with no electricity, no gas and no _____ **water**.

6 The basement was filled with _____ **water** after a night of torrential rain.

Self help

Add the collocates of *water* to your vocabulary notebook.

Vocabulary

Wordlist on page 214 of the Coursebook.

A Attitude adverbials

Underline the correct alternative.

1 These walking boots were *ridiculously/amusingly/funnily* **expensive** – over twice the price of my last pair.

2 It hasn't rained for six weeks and water levels in the reservoirs are *miraculously/worryingly/reassuringly* **low**.

3 Temperatures are *inevitably/naturally/unusually* **high** for this time of year; in some regions over fifteen degrees above the seasonal average.

4 Judy's just phoned to say that Phil's back from his gap year. *Funnily/Rightly/Personally* **enough** I was thinking about him this morning.

5 Government measures to reduce pollution have been *luckily/happily/laughably* **inadequate**.

6 Villagers were *understandably/wisely/sensibly* **upset** at the damage caused by high winds to the church tower.

B Collocations with *work*

For **1–8**, decide which collocation with *work* from the box is being described. You do not need to use all the collocations.

Example: *She works from home doing editorial work for three or four different publishers.*
= freelance work

Work + noun

WORK + permit experience schedule incentive environment

Noun + work

charity consultancy restoration construction conservation + ***WORK***

Adjective + work

freelance social voluntary administrative casual + ***WORK***

---

1 They've planted 5000 trees on the hillside to prevent further soil erosion.

2 We can provide your company with a range of services including strategic planning, project management, marketing planning and quality control.

3 All pupils spend two weeks in the summer term in a local business or industry in order to get a taste of the world of work.

4 They wouldn't renew it when it ran out, and he had to leave the country.

5 She's a civil servant who gives help and advice to people in the community who have financial or family problems.

6 It took eight long years to bring the building back to its former glory.

7 I usually try and get a job in a bar or hotel during the summer holidays.

8 If we go six months without a missing a day, we get an extra day off work in the next six months.

C Approximation

1a Complete the sentences with one word in each gap. The words are used to describe an approximate rather than an exact number.

a _____ 300 000 Australian saltwater crocodiles were killed between 1945 and 1972.

b Worldwide, the legal trade in crocodile skins has _____ tripled since 1977.

c _____ of 90 000 are killed annually in the wild.

b Check your answers in the multiple-choice cloze text on page 159 of the Coursebook.

2 Underline the correct alternative.

1 The company produces *just/such/something* like 2000 tons of the stuff every day.

2 He should be out of hospital in a week or *approximately/about/so*.

3 *Extremely/Very/Quite* nearly 85 per cent of those surveyed said they were in favour of the proposal.

4 *Just/Some/Few* under three per cent said they were undecided.

5 I reckon we'll get there *so/something/round* about six o'clock, don't you?

6 It's a very exclusive area, with houses costing *upwards/more/over* of £750 000.

7 They estimate there were *many/some/plenty* two and a half million people at the demonstration; that's over half the population of the entire city.

8 She probably earns *something/round/upwards* in the region of £80 000 a year.

Language focus

Grammar reference on pages 223–224 of the Coursebook.

A Conjunctions

Rewrite the sentences using the words given. There is an example at the beginning **(0)**.

0 She wore dark glasses because she didn't want to be recognized. **(so that)**

   She wore dark glasses so that she wouldn't be recognized.

1 I don't like boxing, but I still enjoyed the film *Ali*. **(even)**

   _____

2 Two of their players were sent off, but they still won the game. **(despite)**

   _____

3 If we don't phone her, she'll worry about us. **(otherwise)**

   _____

4 It doesn't matter how I comb it, my hair always looks a mess! **(however)**

   _____

5 You might want some more later, so I'll leave the plate there. **(in case)**

   _____

6 We spoke very quietly because we didn't want to wake my dad up. **(so as)**

   _____

B Modal verbs

For questions **1–8** below, use the information in **a** to complete the gap in **b**, which is more formal. Choose from the words in the box. There is an example at the beginning **(0)**.

> obliged   recommended   obligatory   supposed   ~~obligation~~
> required   permitted   presumed   forbidden

0 a We don't have to give the money back.

  b We are under no _obligation_ to refund the money.

1 a You mustn't smoke anywhere in the building.

  b Smoking is not _____ in any part of the building.

2 a They've been told they mustn't speak to the press.

  b They have been _____ to speak to the press.

3 a You really should wear strong shoes.

  b Sturdy footwear is strongly _____ .

4 a You needn't pay until the course finishes.

  b Payment is not _____ until the end of the course.

5 a Don't feel you have to give anything.

  b You should not feel _____ to contribute.

6 a It should have got here a couple of weeks ago.

  b It was _____ to arrive a fortnight ago.

7 a They think he must have left the country.

  b He is _____ to have left the country.

8 a You must wear a seat belt.

  b The wearing of seat belts is _____ .

Reading and Use of English
Part 1

Multiple-choice cloze

For questions **1–8**, read the text below and decide which answer (**A**, **B**, **C** or **D**) best fits each gap. There is an example at the beginning **(0)**.

World's oldest dinosaur

Scientists have confirmed that a set of fossilized bones, first **(0)** ...... in the 1930s in Tanzania and then sent to London's Natural History Museum to be **(1)** ...... ,are those of a Labrador-sized dinosaur that lived at least 10 to 15 million years earlier than the previous oldest-known dinosaur. Having recently examined the fossils, the scientists have **(2)** ...... that the dinosaur probably stood **(3)** ...... on two legs and was about three metres long. They also found the creature's arm bones **(4)** ...... the key characteristics of dinosaurs and that it must have grown rapidly, another distinguishing **(5)** ...... of dinosaurs. However, they do not know whether it was a carnivore or herbivore because no teeth or jaws have been **(6)** .... The research team believe that their findings **(7)** ...... that dinosaurs evolved earlier than many believe as the fossils have been **(8)** ...... to between 247 million and 235 million years ago, a geological period known as the Triassic when Africa was part of a giant supercontinent called Pangaea, which included South America, the Antarctic and Australia.

0 A revealed   **B** exposed   **C** unearthed   **D** exhumed
1 A housed   **B** deposited   **C** collected   **D** stored
2 A concluded   **B** thought   **C** outlined   **D** figured
3 A upright   **B** vertical   **C** upward   **D** raised
4 A carry   **B** display   **C** illustrate   **D** involve
5 A aspect   **B** part   **C** feature   **D** point
6 A rescued   **B** preserved   **C** sustained   **D** conserved
7 A support   **B** back   **C** maintain   **D** establish
8 A identified   **B** tracked   **C** dated   **D** traced

Open cloze

For questions **1–8**, read the text below and think of the word which best fits each gap. Use only **one** word in each gap. There is an example at the beginning **(0)**.

Write your answers **IN CAPITAL LETTERS**.

Life after Man: A vision of the future

What if humans **(0)** ...*WERE*... wiped out? Luckily for the world after humans, not all big mammals would be gone. A continent-sized museum, Africa, still holds **(1)** .... can be described as a striking collection. If **(2)** .... were no people left, Africa, **(3)** .... has been occupied by humans longer than any other place, would revert **(4)** .... the purest primeval state on Earth but it would see some key changes. For a start, North African cattle were once wild, **(5)** .... after thousands of years with humans, they've been cross-bred to develop huge stomachs. This is **(6)** .... they can eat huge amounts during the day, because it's too dangerous to graze at night. Consequently, they're not very quick. Left on their own, **(7)** .... human protection, they'd be vulnerable. And as cattle now account for more than half **(8)** .... live weight of African savannah ecosystems, they would provide a feast for lions and hyenas. Once cows were gone, there would be more than double the feed for everything else.

Word formation

For questions **1–8**, use the word given in capitals at the end of some of the lines to form a word that fits in the gap **in the same line**. There is an example at the beginning **(0)**.

Write your answers **IN CAPITAL LETTERS**.

Rainforest Concern

Frustrated and tired of hearing about the **(0)** ...*DISAPPEARING*... rainforests? Well here's your chance to do something positive about it.
The world's rainforests represent a vast reservoir of **(1)** .... and
hold potential for the **(2)** .... of new medicines and foods. There is
no doubt that large-scale deforestation alters the climate: it **(3)** ....
droughts in the dry season and floods in the rainy season. The result is
fewer animal and plant species, soil **(4)** .... , a water supply which is
(5) .... and poorer health for the local people. By joining Rainforest
Concern, a registered charity, and sponsoring acres of **(6)** ....
rainforest for the Choco-Andean Rainforest Corridor in Ecuador, you will
be protecting one of the world's most important ecological areas. Within
these forests live a high number of seriously **(7)** .... species of animals,
birds and plants, many of which are found nowhere else on earth. You will
also be helping to secure the **(8)** .... and culture of the Awa and
Cayapas indigenous people, who still live in harmony with their natural
environment.

APPEAR

KNOW
DISCOVER
INTENSE

ERODE
RELY
THREAT

DANGER

SURVIVE

Key word transformation

For questions **1–6**, complete the second sentence so that it has a similar meaning to the first sentence, using the word given. **Do not change the word given.** Use between **three** and **six** words, including the word given. There is an example at the beginning **(0)**.

Write your answers **IN CAPITAL LETTERS**.

0 I'm sure a burglar came into our house while we were sleeping and stole the jewellery then.

BROKEN

Someone ..... *MUST HAVE BROKEN INTO* ..... the house while we were sleeping and stolen the jewellery then.

1 Firefighters need to ensure their equipment works perfectly as their lives depend on it.

ORDER

Firefighters need to keep their equipment .... as their lives depend on it.

2 It's possible that the shops will sell all their bottled water so we should buy all we need now.

CASE

We should buy all the bottled water we need now .... out of it.

3 If we don't act now, it's possible there will be no more tigers left within a few years.

OTHERWISE

We need to act now .... out within a few years.

4 Even though Diego didn't know any French at all, he managed to communicate with the Parisian taxi driver.

SINGLE

Despite .... French, Diego managed to communicate with the Parisian taxi driver.

5 I wish I hadn't let Max borrow my money because none of his investments has shown a profit.

NEVER

I ought .... my money to Max because none of his investments has shown a profit.

6 You won't get the job as manager if you don't spend time improving your communication skills.

WORK

You won't be promoted to .... communication skills.

Proposal

1 Read the following Writing Part 2 task, then complete each of the gaps in the model answer with one of the words or expressions from the box. There is an example at the beginning **(0)**.

The local authority in the town where you are studying has announced its intention to increase the annual budget for environmental projects next year. As a member of a local environmental group you have been asked to submit a proposal for the authorities giving your suggestions. You should give details of how the money should be spent in at least **three** areas, including clear reasons for your recommendations.

Write your **proposal** in 220–260 words.

therefore	~~the first of these~~	whilst	instead	this has led to	
clearly	as	also	as well as	in order to	finally

Recommendations for environmental projects for the town of Didcup

INTRODUCTION

It is gratifying to observe that the local authority has decided to increase its financial commitment to environmental projects. There are three main areas requiring urgent attention and funding.

REDUCING POLLUTION

(0) _The first of these_ is the unacceptably high level of pollution caused by exhaust fumes from cars and lorries. **(1)** _____ a higher incidence of respiratory illness among local inhabitants and a decline in the number of tourists visiting Didcup.

A substantial proportion of the budget should **(2)** _____ be allocated to the creation of more pedestrianized areas within the main shopping district. Money might **(3)** _____ be spent on an awareness-raising campaign, encouraging people to leave their cars at home and use public transport **(4)** _____ .

GREEN AREAS

(5) _____ Didcup boasts a number of parks and gardens, there is a noticeable lack of trees, bushes and flowers on the pavements of our residential areas. **(6)** _____ the obvious aesthetic benefits of these plants to the town, they would release more oxygen into the atmosphere and help in the fight against pollution. **(7)** _____ , funds would also need to be set aside for the maintenance of these areas.

WILDLIFE PROTECTION

(8) _____ , some of the budget should be devoted to the preservation of the town's wildlife. Especially at risk are hedgehogs, hundreds of which are killed each year by traffic. **(9)** _____ protect these highly vulnerable animals, traffic signs could be erected warning drivers to look out for them. This would greatly benefit our gardens **(10)** _____ hedgehogs help control unwanted slugs and snails.

Indeed, all of these measures will make Didcup a much better place for everyone, whether they are resident or tourist, human or animal.

2 In the box below write those expressions from the model which refer to spending or using money.

> _increased its financial commitment to_
> _____
> _____
> _____
> _____

3 Either: **a** write your own answer to the task in exercise **1** or **b** write one of the following proposals.

1 The principal of your college has been given a budget for the improvement of the learning environment in your college. Write a proposal for your principal, giving details of how the money should be spent in at least three areas and including clear reasons for your recommendations.

2 Your manager at work has been given a budget for the improvement of the working environment in your branch or department. Write a proposal for your manager, giving details of how the money should be spent in at least three areas and including clear reasons for your recommendations.

Don't forget!

• Plan your answer carefully.
• As in the model, use a range of vocabulary, structures and linking expressions.
• Write between 220 and 260 words.

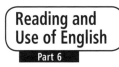

Food for thought

Cross-text multiple matching

1 You are going to read extracts from four different books on common rituals. For questions **1–4** on page 101, choose from the extracts **A–D**. The extracts may be chosen more than once.

Common food rituals

Four writers discuss the different roles that food plays in our lives.

A

It is because of its centrality in our lives that food and the sourcing, hunting, growing, preparing and consumption of it lend themselves so well to ritual. Some customs are so entrenched within culture that we are not always confident of their origins. An example of this are the food restrictions that feature in the major religions. From an anthropological perspective, these are often explained as having once been mechanisms for conserving resources as well as a means of preserving hygiene in pre-industrial communities. Only later did the spiritual associations overtake the practical factors. By no means does this theory have universal support, but evident in the modern world is that, religion aside, people will choose to reject certain foods to mark social boundaries; class, wealth, ethical viewpoint, and so on. It is also apparent that the more we move towards secular living, the less our old rituals appear to matter; no longer is there a necessity to partake of a meal in a wider group setting.

B

In the past, the sharing of a meal had an inseparably social and religious purpose, with the largest feasts marking key passages of life; birth, marriage and death. Although the child might have been the focal point of a baptism, or the deceased the subject of the funeral, the 'audience' was not peripheral. Rather it was their unification which was the goal of the shared meal. Even until the last century, the tradition of younger generations returning to the matriarchal home for the ritual weekly gathering and grandmother's cooking was still prevalent. It seems, rather sadly, that this has been abandoned, perhaps in favour of other pursuits. What is interesting, however, is that many people still adhere to rules concerning prohibited foods; religion is still central in governing what is regarded as fit to be consumed, or not. Thus it seems that food and the spiritual path are intertwined.

C

Foods considered sacred and taboo have been defined by religion; they provided a means of becoming closer to God and for many this remains their function today. Rituals involving food can be equally significant to their practitioners. The Japanese tea ceremony earns recognition as a cultural treasure through the sheer art of its performance. The 'Christmas Pudding', with its origins in medieval England, is no less an emblem of culinary tradition. Despite the very obvious differences between a subtle green tea and a spicy rich dessert, there is a commonality; the meaningfulness given to each stage of creation through the rituals of movement, of ingredient, of a recipe or procedure followed. In contrast, we have developed a hasty and mechanical approach to the making of meals and with it, a disconnection to the real value of food and what it represents beyond our basic survival. Not all is lost. There appears to be a resurgence of interest in the concept of cooking and providing for the larger group; and it is this phenomenon that I intend to explore.

D

In sharing a meal, we reinforce the ties that bind us to family, friends, associates, or even larger social groups. Historically, the choice of foods that could or could not be eaten was religion's way of creating identity and group cohesion, and in most cases, the exclusion of foods from a diet continues to be a deliberate act of worship. But whether you are religious or otherwise, there is a good chance that the meals that you make ready for yourself, or which have been made ready for you, have been produced with little thought and attention. It is time-efficiency that is valued in the modern era, not mastery and skill or labour performed with love. And as the craftsmanship involved with food continues to die out, so do the celebrations that bring people together. Must we be doomed to a life of flavoured pills eaten in self-inflicted solitary confinement?

Which writer

expresses a different opinion from the others on why communities now avoid certain foods?	1	
has a similar opinion to writer D on the significance of communal eating?	2	
has a different view from the others regarding the extent to which communal eating continues as a social feature?	3	
takes a similar view to writer C with regard to the preparation of food?	4	

2 a Complete each gap with **two words** so that the second sentence has the same meaning as the first. Some words are highlighted in **bold** to help you.

0 The preparing and consumption of food are very suitable for ritual.

The preparing and consumption of food **lend** _themselves well_ **to** ritual. (A)

1 A common explanation for food restrictions is that they were once mechanisms for conserving resources.

Food restrictions **are** often _____ **having once been** mechanisms for conserving resources. (A)

2 The spiritual associations did not overtake the practical factors until later.

Only _____ the spiritual associations overtake the practical factors. (A)

3 This theory does not in any way have universal support.

By _____ does this theory have universal support. (A)

4 People have abandoned family meals in order to do other things.

Family meals have been abandoned **in** _____ other pursuits. (B)

5 Interestingly, many people still adhere to rules concerning prohibited foods.

_____ **interesting is that** many people still adhere to rules concerning prohibited foods. (B)

6 The Christmas Pudding is just as much an emblem of culinary tradition as the Japanese tea ceremony.

The Christmas Pudding is _____ an emblem of culinary tradition **than** the Japanese tea ceremony. (C)

7 It is likely that the meals have been produced with little thought and attention.

There is _____ **chance** that the meals have been produced with little thought and attention. (D)

8 The celebrations that bring people together die out at the same time as the craftsmanship involved with food.

As the craftsmanship involved with food dies out, _____ the celebrations that bring people together. (D)

b Check your answers in the reading text. The relevant section is given in brackets.

Vocabulary

Wordlist on page 214 of the Coursebook.

A Phrasal verbs and prepositions

In **a** and **b** below, complete the sentences with one of the prepositions from the relevant box. There is an example at the beginning **(0)**.

a Eating and drinking

at   off   down   ~~up~~   up

0 She heated _up_ some of the previous day's stew in the microwave.

1 I polished _____ the remains of that chocolate cake when I got home last night – I was so hungry!

2 When he noticed the time, he gulped _____ the rest of his tea and hurried out.

3 She sat at the table looking sad and dejected, just picking _____ her food.

4 I often go for a run in the morning to work _____ an appetite for breakfast.

b Deception

at   for   into   on

1 He was tricked _____ signing the document, which effectively handed over possession of his house to his nephew.

2 Let's play a trick _____ Stuart – we'll hide all his shoes in the washing machine!

3 My brother confessed to me that he used to cheat _____ cards when we were younger.

4 They've promised us a salary increase if we agree to work overtime, but we're not falling _____ their tricks anymore – we know what they're up to.

B Expressions with *eat*

1 Complete the expressions in **bold** with an appropriate noun from the box.

bird   hand   home   horse   profits   words

1 When my son and his family come to stay they usually **eat us out of house and _____** : it costs us a small fortune!

2 Judy, our accountant, **has got** the boss **eating out of her _____** : she can get him to do anything she wants.

3 The increase in shoplifting from the company's city centre stores has **eaten into its _____** quite considerably.

4 I always said he'd be a failure, but I was **made to eat my _____** recently when I read he'd become a millionaire three times over.

5 Is dinner nearly ready? I **could eat a _____** !

6 I don't know how that child puts on weight – she **eats like a _____** .

2 Match the expressions in **1–6** of exercise **1** with an appropriate meaning **a–e**.
Example: 1 c

a make someone like you so much they do whatever you want

b be forced to admit you were wrong about something

c eat a lot of someone's food when you are a guest in their home

d eat very little

e be extremely hungry

f use up or reduce a part of something, especially time or money

C Intensifiers

Match each sentence beginning **1–8** with an appropriate ending **a–h**.

1 All the flights to Manchester were **fully**	**a keen** to get back to work.
2 His new film is a convincing and **deeply**	**b booked**, so we flew to Heathrow instead.
3 The weather suddenly turned **bitterly**	**c exhausted**, and we all went straight to bed.
4 My teenage son is a proud and **fiercely**	**d influential** scientific papers on the subject.
5 Dr Amalric has written several **highly**	**e moving** tale of one man's battle with alcoholism.
6 He's slowly recovering and **desperately**	**f cold**, thanks to a chill wind coming from the east.
7 Her next opponent is the **comparatively**	**g unknown** Pat Dale, who has yet to win a championship.
8 The long, hot walk left us feeling **utterly**	**h independent** child, but he still likes a cuddle from his mum.

Self help

Study the adverb + adjective collocations in **bold** in the exercise above for one minute. Then cover the sentence endings a–f and look only at the beginnings 1–6. How many collocations can you remember?

Language focus

 Grammar reference on page 224 of the Coursebook.

Comparisons

In each of the following sentences one of the words is incorrect. Find the word and change it. There is an example at the beginning **(0)**.

0 The food wasn't quite as spicy as I'd been told it might be and overall I enjoyed the meal, as ~~had~~ everyone else in my family.
        did

1 By far the dullest job I've ever had was when I worked like a security guard in a high street clothes shop in Macclesfield.

2 It wasn't so much Ralph's good looks which appealed to Eleanor and attracted her to him than his warm effervescent personality.

3 Everyone said the listening exam was much more difficult than they thought it would be, but I didn't think it was anywhere close as hard as the ones we'd done in class.

4 I much prefer our local supermarket to any of those huge out-of-town hypermarkets: apart from being a great amount more convenient, it's quite a lot cheaper, too.

5 I can't understand why the film was such hugely successful: it wasn't nearly as good as his last one, yet it made five times as much at the box office.

6 The more freedom you give children and the fewer limits you impose on them, the more unruly they become, in much the same way that certain types of plant, which will overrun a garden if they are not regularly cut back and held in check.

Multiple-choice cloze

For questions **1–8**, read the text below and decide which answer (**A**, **B**, **C** or **D**) best fits each gap. There is an example at the beginning (**0**).

Calorie levels on food packaging

(**0**) ...... to some nutritionists, calorie levels printed on food packaging are (**1**) .... Manufacturers' measurements of energy levels in their food do not, for example, include fibre, which makes up about five per cent of our calorie (**2**) ....

Dieters who eat muesli for breakfast may wonder why they are (**3**) ...... to lose weight, because the packaging ignores 'invisible calories' in its high fibre content. In contrast, those eating large (**4**) ...... of protein may be taking in less energy than they realize because the (**5**) ...... system overestimates the number of calories it contains by 20 per cent.

Nutrition advice also fails to (**6**) ...... for whether the food is raw or cooked and processed or unprocessed. Cooking and processing food can (**7**) ...... calorie levels by up to 30 per cent because we burn more energy digesting things which are hard and uncooked. It means people trying to stick to the daily recommended calorie limits of 2500 for men and 2000 for women may be taking in (**8**) ...... more or less energy than they realize.

0	**A** Regarding	**B** Concerning	**C** Respecting	**D** <u>According</u>
1	**A** miscalculating	**B** miscounting	**C** misleading	**D** misjudging
2	**A** inlet	**B** input	**C** income	**D** intake
3	**A** aiming	**B** struggling	**C** attempting	**D** forcing
4	**A** numbers	**B** limits	**C** amounts	**D** deals
5	**A** actual	**B** contemporary	**C** current	**D** recent
6	**A** account	**B** justify	**C** reason	**D** explain
7	**A** amend	**B** alter	**C** adapt	**D** adjust
8	**A** importantly	**B** significantly	**C** respectively	**D** correspondingly

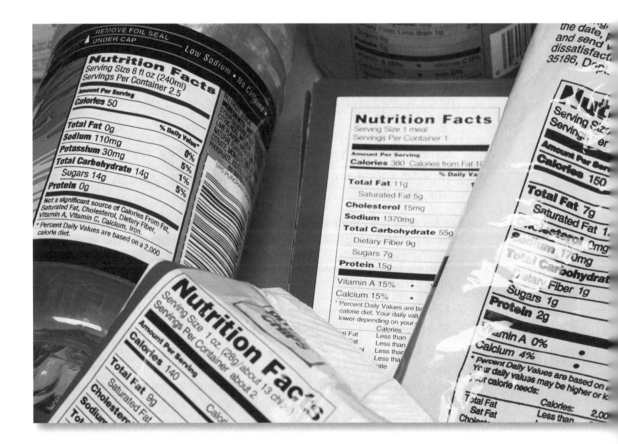

Open cloze

For questions **1–8**, read the text below and think of the word which best fits each gap. Use only **one** word in each gap. There is an example at the beginning **(0)**.

Write your answers **IN CAPITAL LETTERS**.

Science studies why some foods are so moreish

Scientists are unravelling the mystery of **(0)** ...WHY.. some snacks seem impossible to eat in small amounts. Some might call **(1)** .... greed, but another name for such behaviour is hedonic hyperphagia, the scientific term for 'eating to excess for pleasure'. **(2)** .... the term can refer to the recreational over-eating that occurs in almost **(3)** .... at some point in life, the chronic form is one of the key factors lying **(4)** .... the obesity epidemic. Researcher Tobias Hoch scanned the brains of rats as they ate potato chips and ordinary pellets; **(5)** .... the fat and carbohydrates mixture containing the same number of calories, the rats were far keener on the crisps, with the reward and addiction centres in their brains **(6)** .... most active as they ate this kind of snack. 'The effect of potato chips on brain activity can only partially be explained **(7)** .... their fat and carbohydrate content,' said Hoch. 'There must be something else in the chips making **(8)** .... so desirable.' Pinpointing the molecular triggers in snacks that stimulate the reward centres could lead to the development of pharmaceutical drugs that combat over-eating.

Word formation

For questions **1–8** read the text below. Use the word given in capitals at the end of some of the lines to form a word that fits in the gap **in the same line**. There is an example at the beginning **(0)**. Write your answers **IN CAPITAL LETTERS**.

> **Don't forget!**
> * Look at the words before and after each space to help you choose the correct part of speech.
> * You may need to use the negative or plural form of a noun.
> * You may need to use the negative form of an adjective or adverb.

A vegetarian cookbook

If you often have **(0)** ..DIFFICULTY.. knowing what to serve for a mixed gathering of vegetarians and non-vegetarians, *Vegetarian Dishes for All* is a definite must-have. Its **(1)** .... range of mouth-watering soups, starters, salads, pasta dishes, gratins and desserts provides ample **(2)** .... to the most sceptical of meat-eaters that vegetarian food is not automatically dull in flavour or **(3)** .... in appearance. The recipes, which are **(4)** .... straightforward, will teach both the novice and the expert how to cook vegetables creatively and with spectacular results. Easy-to-find ingredients are used in a wide range of inspiring **(5)** .... , which will delight every one of your guests, and elevate your cooking skills to new **(6)** .... There's also a special chapter for parents, with an impressive and tasty selection of recipes aimed at **(7)** .... even the **(8)** .... of young eaters to meet their daily requirement of vegetables.

DIFFICULT
IMAGINE
PROVE
ATTRACT
REFRESH
COMBINE
HIGH
COURAGE
FUSS

Key word transformation

For questions **1–6**, complete the second sentence so that it has a similar meaning to the first sentence, using the word given. **Do not change the word given.** Use between **three** and **six** words, including the word given. There is an example at the beginning **(0)**.

Write your answers **IN CAPITAL LETTERS**.

0 Climbing when you're hungry is a bad idea.

EMPTY

Climbing on ...*AN EMPTY STOMACH IS NOT*.... recommended.

1 Jack got really hungry while he was training in the gym.

APPETITE

Jack worked .... his training session in the gym.

2 The key to a good speech is less about what you say and more about how you say it.

WHAT

The key to a good speech lies not so .... how you say it.

3 Eric's meal was nearly as good as the one the winner made.

CLOSE

Eric's meal came a .... winning dish.

4 This new role allows me to be very independent, unlike my previous one.

CONTRAST

This new role gives me a great deal .... my previous one.

5 The menu suggested that the meal was very spicy, but it wasn't.

NOWHERE

The meal .... as the menu suggested.

6 How did you ever believe a story that was so ridiculous!

FELL

I can't believe that .... ridiculous story!

Essay

1 Read the following Writing Part 1 task. Before you write your answer, do the related language task in exercise **2** below.

Your class has attended a panel discussion on what methods employers could use to encourage young people to work in their restaurants and cafés. You have made the notes below:

> **Methods employers could use to encourage young people to work in their restaurants and cafés.**
>
> - payment
> - training
> - hours

> Some opinions expressed in the discussion:
>
> 'Waiters shouldn't have to depend on tips.'
>
> 'I couldn't get a job because I had no experience.'
>
> 'I need a job that will fit around my college work.'

Write an essay discussing **two** of the methods in your notes. You should **explain which method you think is more important** for employers to consider, **giving reasons** in support of your answer.

You may, if you wish, make use of the opinions expressed in the discussion, but you should use your own words as far as possible.

2 When writing the essay you should try to use a variety of different forms and structures to give your opinions. Underline the correct alternative in the sentences below.

1 It might be *preference/preferable/preferred* for many students if they could work flexible hours.

2 The *establishment/establishing/established* of adequate training courses is a priority.

3 If restaurant owners *ought/have/were* to pay higher salaries , it would do much to mitigate the problem.

4 *Having/To Have/Having been* seen first-hand the value of this course, every student recommended it.

5 It is important *give/to give/giving* every student the best possible opportunity.

6 *No sooner/As soon as/Soon* there is more flexibility about working hours, more students will start applying for jobs.

7 The culture at many workplaces will improve immediately the legislation *will be/is/would be* passed.

8 If café managers were more proactive, the students *must be/can be/could be* relied on to rise to the occasion.

3 Now write your answer in **220–260 words**.

Multiple choice

You are going to read an article about a television series on expensive hotels. For questions **1–6**, choose the answer (**A**, **B**, **C** or **D**) which you think fits best according to the text.

Backstage at the world's best hotels

In his new TV series, actor Richard E Grant unlocks the secrets of five-star service, fine dining and luxury suites. So, what's the key to a truly great stay?

In *Hotel Secrets*, viewers will see Richard E Grant cavorting like a gleeful child around LA's Chateau Marmont, sweeping, awestruck, through Le Royal Monceau in Paris, gasping with appreciation as he surveys the view from the Penthouse Suite in the Four Seasons New York (at more than $40000 a night, one of the most expensive in the world). When we meet, Grant addresses the thorny question of why he's presenting a television series that focuses on the utterly unaffordable during a time of austerity. 'I got my head round it,' he says, 'by thinking that, in the middle of the Depression, Hollywood churned out Fred Astaire and Ginger Rogers fantasy movies. So I think we have an appetite for not being faced by the really grim economic stuff that we're fed on a daily basis.' Indeed, he maintains that having a peek into how people live at that level is voyeuristically interesting to do.

But is the task something he relishes? 'If you are hyper-curious, and you want to find out what goes on in making up a luxury hotel, it's the best job in the world, because you have the advantage of going backstage. The designers, the bellhops, concierges, receptionists, chefs, pastry chefs, cleaners, everything – you get the whole gauge of it. It's exactly the equivalent of a theatre: you've got the front-of-house show of it all, where the performance of the hotel takes place. But everything that is backstage is a world within a world, a hermetically sealed microcosm of people, dedicated to giving five-star service and pleasure.'

The series is certainly escapist. The camera dwells longingly on gleaming Jacuzzis (often occupied by a fully clothed Richard E Grant) or the vast open spaces of luxury suites, on swimming pools, on tinkling fountains, on exotic – or garish – design details. Happily, just when the sheer unattainability of it all is in danger of alienating the viewer, Grant's sheer enthusiasm pulls the show onwards. He seems to have a particular affinity for his interview subjects, roaring with shared laughter or badgering them as the mood takes him. Admittedly, some encounters are friendlier than others. In the first episode, he confesses to a degree of terror when going to meet hotel mogul Donald Trump (who gives a lengthy monologue about the unhygienic tradition of shaking hands, before Grant gets him to confess that he does it anyway so that people won't hate him).

When it gets seriously weird, such as at the Barkley Pet Hotel and Day Spa near Los Angeles, Grant just lets it wash over him. 'When I read the brief beforehand I thought, oh dear: this is Louis Theroux, freak-television stuff,' he says, referring to the documentary maker renowned for his exposé-type programmes. 'But when you go into it you realize there's somebody out there who has got a lot of money and wants their dog to be given five-star treatment and to have closed-circuit television in their little kennel, so that they can see them at all times.' Grant admits that his initial reaction was to scoff and to consider it ludicrous, but his re-evaluation was '… if somebody's providing that service, then why not?'.

Looking back, did he ever imagine that one day he'd be granted a free pass to all this opulence? 'I hoped that I could make a living as an actor. But how I've ended up doing so is beyond anything I could have ever anticipated. I thought I would be lucky if I could work regularly in the theatre, never in a city like London. So it's been beyond all expectations on my part. But you are prepared for it, in that from the moment you start doing movies, the level of luxury in the hotels that you stay in goes from nought to 100 miles an hour instantly. If I'd never done a movie, and I was plonked into this series, I would have been much more wide-eyed.'

Grant lets the viewer draw their own conclusions about the people he meets. 'I kept in the back of my mind that I wanted to be able to go back to all these hotels, and to look the people in the face that I had spoken to, rather than go to the camera behind their backs and say: "This person is an absolute Satanist".' He pokes his nose round the grandest and greatest: The Ritz, The Goring, Waldorf Astoria, Caesar's Palace. But it's all a show, and Grant knows it. 'It's what Napoleon said about a throne being only a bench covered in velvet. The bed that you slept in? Tomorrow night somebody else will be sleeping in it.' As Grant makes clear, that's the great egalitarian nature of staying in a hotel: no matter how fancy it is, it's still a room for hire.

1 In the first paragraph, the writer's purpose is to
   A question the value of making a television series on extreme wealth.
   B allow the presenter to put forward the benefits of watching his series.
   C dismiss the idea that a recession affects people who are very affluent.
   D highlight the reasons why the presenter is ideally suited to the series.

2 What point is exemplified by the references to the theatre and hotels?
   A People in these industries are often perceived of as being insincere.
   B As creative industries, they tend to be more rewarding for employees.
   C The public are kept apart from the way these industries operate.
   D Teamwork is an essential component for the success of these industries.

3 In the third paragraph, the writer suggests that Grant's behaviour
   A might deter some people from watching the entire programme.
   B is more respectful depending on who he is interviewing.
   C re-engages people who might start to lose interest.
   D makes the programme unique within its genre.

4 According to the writer, when Grant first heard about the pet hotel,
   A he was wary of being seen to imitate another presenter's style.
   B he was unsurprised that such a facility could exist.
   C he felt irritated by the superficiality of the animals' owners.
   D he thought that the concept of the hotel was absurd.

5 In the fifth paragraph, Grant says that his acting career
   A had exposed him to the kind of comfort he encountered in the series.
   B had developed his appreciation of more luxurious environments.
   C gave him the sense of confidence required to make the series.
   D meant that he was unwilling to put up with substandard facilities.

6 In the final paragraph, the writer puts forward the view that
   A expensive hotel rooms do not give us the status we imagine.
   B Grant has taken a slightly devious approach with his subjects.
   C the promise of exclusivity will always convince people to pay more.
   D Grant is unlikely to regard this series as a high point of his career.

Vocabulary

Wordlist on page 214 of the Coursebook.

A Money

Complete the sentences with one of the words from the box.

> redundancy   pocket   counterfeit   ransom   sponsorship   housekeeping

1 Several members of a criminal gang have been arrested on charges of printing and passing _____ **money**.

2 Some parents give their children far too much _____ **money** each week.

3 She could never afford to buy meat or fish because her husband used to spend half the _____ **money** before getting home on Friday night.

4 The kidnappers released the hostages two hours after the _____ **money** was paid.

5 The factory where he worked was forced to close down and he used some of his _____ **money** to pay off his mortgage.

6 I swam 163 lengths of the pool non-stop and raised over £500 in _____ **money**, which I donated to a local hospital.

B Verbs usually associated with money

1 For questions **1–5**, underline the correct verb **A**, **B**, **C** or **D**.

1 The discovery of a second set of fingerprints _____ **weight to the theory** that Brooks did not act alone.

   A owes   **B** pays   **C** lends   **D** invests

2 The minister _____ **tribute to** the rescue workers for their 'courage in the face of adversity'.

   A sold   **B** paid   **C** lent   **D** spent

3 I know a quicker way to get there if you want to _____ **some time**.

   A invest   **B** spend   **C** save   **D** borrow

4 The French writer _____ **the idea** for his first novel from an old Russian folk tale.

   A borrowed   **B** bought   **C** saved   **D** charged

5 The company _____ **its success** to the quality of its products.

   A pays   **B** lends   **C** sells   **D** owes

2 Which of the correct verbs in exercise **1** collocates with each group of nouns? Write the infinitive form of the verbs.

1 _____ a compliment/attention/one's respects

2 _____ a favour/an apology/an explanation

3 _____ support/credibility/assistance

4 _____ effort/energy

5 _____ a word/a phrase

> **Self help**
>
> Add the **Verbs usually associated with money** to your vocabulary notebook, together with the nouns which collocate with them.

3 Complete the sentences using appropriate verb and noun collocations from exercise **2**. Write the correct form of the verb, and if necessary, use an article (*a/an*) with the noun. There is an example at the beginning **(0)**.

0 I didn't really hear what he said; I wasn't _paying_ much _attention_ , to be honest.

1 It seems I _____ you _____ ; I doubted your honesty, and clearly I was wrong. I hope you can forgive me.

2 Over a hundred people came to the funeral to _____ their last _____ to the woman who had done so much for the local community.

3 In order to refer to the first night of a film or a play, English has _____ the French _____ 'premiere', meaning 'first'.

4 I had to help him, really – I felt I _____ him _____ for that time he fixed my car for me.

5 When I said your new hairstyle was 'different', it wasn't a criticism: on the contrary, I was _____ you _____ .

Language focus

Grammar reference on page 224 of the Coursebook.

Noun phrases

1 Complete the sentences with one of the words from the box.

chances sense depths sign height source matter state grain pack

1 I keep forgetting people's names; I think it must be **a _____ of age**.

2 It's not exactly **a _____ of life and death**, but I would appreciate it if you could get it done as soon as possible.

3 There wasn't **a _____ of truth** in what he said – his speech was **a _____ of lies** from start to finish.

4 I felt **an enormous _____ of relief** when I heard I'd passed.

5 After the rioting, the government declared **a _____ of emergency**, calling out the troops and imposing a night-time curfew.

6 I have no investments or savings, so the state pension is my only **_____ of income**.

7 Whether you're in **the _____ of winter** or **the _____ of summer**, AirFlow® ensures the temperature inside your home is exactly how you want it.

8 The team's **_____ of promotion** to the First Division suffered a blow yesterday when they lost at home to relegation candidates Bristol City.

2 There is one mistake in each of the following sentences. Find the mistakes and correct them. There is an example at the beginning **(0)**.

     lamb

0 We had ~~lamb's~~ chops for lunch yesterday.

1 I'm going to get another water bottle – I'm really thirsty.

2 He tried to turn the handle of door, but realized he'd been locked in.

3 She didn't have an evidence's scrap to support her accusations.

4 She gave me several useful advice pieces on cooking with pastry.

5 We had to write a three pages essay on the importance of money in today's society.

6 The hotel could only guarantee him a week work.

7 They gazed in wonder at the snow-covered mountains' tops.

8 I read about it in last April edition of *Gardening Monthly*.

Open cloze

For questions **1–8**, read the text below and think of the word which best fits each gap. Use only **one** word in each gap. There is an example at the beginning **(0)**.

Write your answers **IN CAPITAL LETTERS**.

The sales

It is December. The first frost and snow of winter **(0)** _ARE_ upon us and, as **(1)** .... drawn by some mysterious force, otherwise sane, ordinary people are getting up at 5 am **(2)** .... queue for hours in the cold and dark. The sales have begun. Before Christmas!

As mere amateur bargain-hunters have always suspected, **(3)** .... is a black art to sales shopping. Cunning sales veterans, determined to avoid the horrid changing-room queue, do their trying-on weeks **(4)** .... advance. Then, once the doors are flung open, they'll push, elbow and lock coat-hangers with **(5)** .... another to reach the object of their desire. This Darwinian struggle is carried **(6)** .... in a terribly polite way, as everybody else pretends that everybody else is being 'so pushy'. Their treasures clutched to their breast, their cheerfulness is barely disguised, in **(7)** .... of the uncomfortable weight of armfuls of plates, dishes, sheets and towels. The only shadow is the sight of other attractive bargains **(8)** .... picked out by fellow shoppers.

Word formation

For questions **1–10**, read the text below. Use the word given in capitals at the end of some of the lines to form a word that fits in the gap **in the same line**. There is an example at the beginning **(0)**.

Write your answers **IN CAPITAL LETTERS**.

Millionaire cheat

People will often go to incredible **(0)** _LENGTHS_ to get rich quick.	**LONG**
In one unusual case of **(1)** .... , three people were found guilty	**DECEIVE**
of attempting to defraud a television company of a million pounds. Major	
Charles Ingram appeared as a **(2)** .... on the programme *Who*	**CONTEST**
Wants to be a Millionaire? in 2001, when, with the help of his wife, Diana,	
and accomplice Tecwen Whittock, he won the top prize.	
But his winning appearance was never broadcast and the cheque was	
cancelled. Production staff called to the **(3)** .... said they grew	**TRY**
suspicious of Ingram's **(4)** .... hesitations and changes of mind,	**NUMBER**
and became aware of the persistent coughing of a member of the audience.	
The show's host noticed how Ingram often seemed **(5)** .... about	**SURE**
the answers he gave. Whittock, a college lecturer, coughed **(6)**	**STRATEGY**
from his seat to indicate the correct answer as Ingram said the four	
alternatives to each question out loud. A video **(7)** .... of the	**RECORD**
programme was played in court as part of the prosecution case. The	
defendants, who had denied all accusations of **(8)** .... , listened	**HONEST**
impassively as sentence was passed.	

Key word transformation

For questions **1–6**, complete the second sentence so that it has a similar meaning to the first sentence, using the word given. **Do not change the word given.** Use between **three** and **six** words, including the word given. There is an example at the beginning **(0)**.

Write your answers **IN CAPITAL LETTERS**.

0 When I caught my boyfriend reading my emails, I felt he had invaded my privacy.

AN

When I caught my boyfriend reading my emails, I regarded it
...... *AS AN INVASION OF* .... my privacy.

1 We would like you to pay for the delivery of this special order before you receive it.

IF

We would appreciate .... advance for the delivery of this special order.

2 Scientists think that there is nothing on that planet to suggest there is any life there.

SIGN

According to scientists, there appears .... life on that planet.

3 It is now 24 hours since Mr William's boat sank and people think there is little likelihood he will survive.

CHANCES

It is now 24 hours since Mr Williams's boat sank and his
.... to be slim.

4 I regret not having the feeling of achieving anything after reaching the summit but I was too exhausted.

SENSE

I wish I .... after reaching the summit but I was too exhausted.

5 Although the job meant that he earned money regularly, Tony did not enjoy it.

REGULAR

Although the job provided him .... of income, Tony did not enjoy it.

6 Monica said that she had bought the item without thinking carefully about it.

PURCHASE

Monica admitted to .... impulse.

Writing | **Part 2**

Proposal

Read the Writing Paper (Part 2) below. Before you write your answer, do the key vocabulary exercises below.

Choose **one** of the following writing tasks. Write your answer in **220–260** words in an appropriate style.

1 You see this announcement in an international magazine called *Consumer Today*.

> ## Good and bad recent purchases
>
> Consumers have so much choice these days that it can feel overwhelming. To help your fellow consumers out, we are asking readers to write a review of two products they have recently purchased, one they are happy with and one that's been disappointing.
>
> Send in a **review** which describes one good and one bad recent purchase you have made and give reasons for these choices.

Write your **review**.

2 The students at your college want a gym to be set up on the campus.

You have been asked to write a proposal for the college director explaining why a gym would be popular with the students and how it would complement the existing sporting facilities.

Write your **proposal**.

3 You are studying at a language school in the UK. You receive this message from an ex-classmate who is currently visiting your home town.

> I'd love a few ideas about things to do. Places to avoid? It'd be fantastic to meet up with someone local. The only thing is, I'm on a really tight budget. I've got my bike for transport. Hope you can email right away.

Write your **email**.

Key vocabulary

Task 1

1 Match each of the adjectives **1–6** with the most appropriate noun **a–f**.
Example: 1 c

1 confusing		**a** components
2 faulty		**b** maintenance
3 misleading		**c** instructions
4 inexplicable		**d** advertising
5 regular		**e** service
6 rude		**f** delay

2 Complete the sentences with one of the words from the box.

design   money
service   warranty
technology   price

1 The product is great but best of all is the **affordable** _____ .
2 It's absolutely the latest **cutting-edge** _____ .
3 The **stylish** _____ has made all my friends envious.
4 You can't argue with the fact that it's **great value for** _____ .
5 They provide comprehensive **after-sales** _____ for all their products.
6 The **three-year** _____ gives consumers peace of mind.

Task 2

1 Which of these words describe the tone or attitude you should adopt in your proposal? You can choose more than one word.

abrupt appreciative negative constructive complaining polite friendly derisive reasonable argumentative concise persuasive sycophantic

2 Replace the informal words in brackets with words from the box.

investing in large number conducted begin construction of enthusiastic perhaps there could be unsatisfactory am confident allow students to

1 A _____ (lot) of students I spoke to were _____ (happy) about the idea.

2 I _____ (really think) a gym would be popular based on the survey I have _____ (done).

3 _____ (Why don't we have) extended opening hours as this would _____ (give us the chance to) use the facilities before and after lectures.

4 I would recommend _____ (getting) some new high-quality rowing machines as some of the cheaper ones on the market ones are _____ (useless).

5 I hope that it will be possible to _____ (get on with) the new gym over the next few months.

3 For **1–3**, cross out the word in *italics* which does **not** collocate with the words in **bold**.
  1 a *useful/welcome/valuable/suited/worthwhile* **addition**.
  2 a/an *serious/general/short/distinct/obvious* **lack of** fitness facilities.
  3 a/an *great/clear/real/complete/urgent* **need for** more fitness facilities.

Task 3

Complete the sentences with one of the verbs from the box, then match each sentence beginning **1–5** with the most appropriate ending **a–e**.

take splash stroll hike soak

1 If I were you, I'd gently _____ along the river bank in the evening

2 Why don't you _____ up the culture in the museum and gallery

3 I know you're on a budget but you could _____ out and go to the Jazz Club

4 It's quite steep but you should definitely _____ up City Peak

5 Then you could _____ in the sights of the Old Town

a because the atmosphere is really lively.
b to enjoy the sunset and feed the ducks.
c because it's amazingly well-preserved.
d to see the breathtaking views of the city.
e because admission is free for students.

Listening bank

1 Aiming high

Listening
Part 1 **Multiple choice** **1.1–1.3**

You will hear three different extracts. For questions **1–6**, choose the answer (**A**, **B** or **C**) which fits best according to what you hear. There are two questions for each extract.

Extract 1

You hear two university students talking about applying for jobs.

1 How does the man feel about applying for jobs?

  A confident he will get the job he wants

  B pleased that his CV looks impressive

  C surprised to have received so many replies

2 The woman has delayed applying for jobs because

  A she may do further study.

  B she might take time off to travel.

  C she could work in the family business.

Extract 2

You hear two business colleagues discussing a conference they have just attended.

3 According to the woman, one of the best things about the conference was

  A the range of backgrounds of the speakers

  B the chance to ask questions after each presentation

  C the large number of people who attended

4 Before the conference began, the man had felt

  A determined to hear one particular presentation.

  B regretful that some presentations had been cancelled.

  C concerned that the programme was too ambitious.

Extract 3

You hear part of a radio discussion in which two people are talking about plans to expand the size of their city.

5 What aspect of the plans does the man criticize?

  A the cost of new public transport initiatives

  B the types of new housing to be built

  C the provision of recreational facilities

6 Both speakers agree that the planned expansion

  A will give the city a stronger sense of identity.

  B will be good for the country as a whole.

  C will improve the international profile of the city.

Times change

Listening
Part 2

Sentence completion **1.4**

You will hear a student giving a presentation about how photography has changed over time. For questions **1–8**, complete the sentences with a word or short phrase.

How photography has changed

In the 1850s, 'wet collodion' photography showed **(1)** .... for the first time.

'Pictorialist' photographers manipulated images, for example by giving them **(2)** ....

In the 1920s, photographs of California's **(3)** .... became world famous.

At the same time, photography was used to reject **(4)** .... in Europe.

Between the two World Wars, the work of 'humanist' photographers appeared in **(5)** ....

In the 1960s, photographers wanted people to have a strong **(6)** .... when they saw their photos.

The **(7)** .... of photographs changed dramatically around the year 2000.

Nowadays, **(8)** .... is nearly always accompanied by photography of some kind.

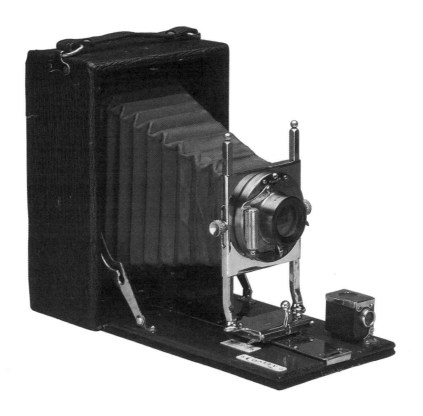

3 Gathering information

Listening Part 3 **Multiple choice** **1.5**

You will hear an interview with a woman called Olivia Hadfield who has been researching how colours can be used to communicate different messages. For questions **1–6**, choose the answer (**A**, **B**, **C** or **D**) which fits best according to what you hear.

1 Olivia says that she first got involved with researching colour
   A because she hoped to further her career in marketing.
   B because she desired a change of lifestyle.
   C to oppose something she thought was unfair.
   D because she felt that businesses underrated the influence of colour.

2 What point does Olivia make about colours and brands?
   A Many people form a subconscious connection between them.
   B Not all products can be successfully branded by a single colour.
   C Some nationalities are more susceptible to colour branding than others.
   D Corporations are happy to market many brands with the same colour.

3 What does Olivia say about our associations with certain colours?
   A Red has the widest range of associations.
   B People have neutral associations with black.
   C Our associations with blue are most rational.
   D White has the most positive associations.

4 Olivia thinks that the link between colour and taste is
   A very well understood.
   B difficult to explain.
   C stronger for foods than drinks.
   D largely based on instinct.

5 When Olivia talks about house colours in her city she is
   A surprised by changing trends.
   B worried about visual pollution.
   C cautious about being unconventional.
   D disappointed by the lack of variety.

6 What aspect of colour would Olivia like to study in future?
   A how climate affects the colours we see
   B how human sight has evolved over time
   C how colour is partly a cultural construct
   D how non-human and human sight differs

Work time

Listening
Part 4

Multiple matching ◉ **1.6–1.10**

You will hear five short extracts in which students are talking about their holiday jobs.
While you listen you must complete both tasks.

TASK ONE

For questions **1–5**, choose from the list **(A–H)** the holiday job that each student did.

A   factory worker

B   waiter in hotel   Speaker 1   ☐ 1

C   worker in tourist information office   Speaker 2   ☐ 2

D   cleaner in hotel   Speaker 3   ☐ 3

E   dairy farm worker   Speaker 4   ☐ 4

F   tour guide   Speaker 5   ☐ 5

G   supermarket checkout staff

H   fruit picker

TASK TWO

For questions **6–10**, choose from the list **(A–H)** the aspect of the job the student liked.

A   receiving positive feedback

B   flexible working hours

C   supportive employer   Speaker 1   ☐ 6

D   friendships with workmates   Speaker 2   ☐ 7

E   good pay rate   Speaker 3   ☐ 8

F   how easily they got the job   Speaker 4   ☐ 9

G   good work experience for later career   Speaker 5   ☐ 10

H   variety of tasks

5 Getting on

 Listening **Part 1** **Multiple choice** **1.11–1.13**

You will hear three different extracts. For questions **1–6**, choose the answer **(A, B** or **C)** which fits best according to what you hear. There are two questions for each extract.

Extract 1

You hear two workmates talking about their older sisters.

1 The man sees his sister regularly because
  A she is his best friend.
  B they enjoy the same activities.
  C her house is close to his.

2 Why does the woman wish she saw her sister more often?
  A She appreciates her sister's sense of humour.
  B She would like her sister's advice and guidance.
  C She enjoys seeing her sister's children.

Extract 2

You hear two neighbours discussing plans to build a wind farm near their houses.

3 What aspect of the wind farm worries the woman?
  A the noise it will make when operating
  B the disruption while it is being installed
  C the visual effect on the landscape

4 Both speakers agree that the wind farm
  A will go ahead regardless of protests.
  B is less desirable than another option.
  C should be built on another site.

Extract 3

You hear an older man and a younger woman discussing changing attitudes to manners.

5 What change in manners does the man disapprove of?
  A not saying thank you
  B not giving up seats for women
  C not eating in a certain way

6 Both speakers agree that queuing
  A is rarely done these days.
  B is popular with the elderly.
  C is a cultural convention.

6 All in the mind?

Sentence completion 1.14

You will hear a psychologist called David Smart talking about the link between creativity and eccentric behaviour. For questions **1–8**, complete the sentences with a word or a short phrase.

Are creative people more likely to behave in an eccentric or unusual way?

David says that **(1)** .... were something that physicist Isaac Newton avoided.

According to David, the author Charles Dickens believed he was being pursued by

(2) ....

David refers to a 1966 study that showed that eccentricity was a **(3)** .... condition.

David says that eccentric/creative people cannot **(4)** .... information so they may behave strangely.

According to David, Anton Strue is researching why eccentric/creative people are more likely to be **(5)** .... than other people.

Strue concluded that eccentric/creative people receive more information, especially

(6) .... , which affects behaviour.

David believes that eccentric/creative people today have more opportunities because of the **(7)** .... industry.

David hopes that more university degrees will include **(8)** .... to promote 'eccentric' ways of thinking.

7 Feeling good

Listening
Part 3

Multiple choice **1.15**

You will hear an interview with a man called Clyde Wilson, a solo sailor, who has crossed both the Atlantic and Pacific Oceans alone in a small sailing boat. For questions **1–6**, choose the answer (**A**, **B**, **C** or **D**) which fits best according to what you hear.

1 What does Clyde say about his motivations for solo sailing?
  A He was inspired to do it by a relative.
  B He has sought different rewards over time.
  C He was challenged by the technical difficulties.
  D He has always wanted to set new sailing records.

2 Clyde tried to avoid accidents by
  A avoiding storms and bad weather.
  B wearing special protective clothing.
  C staying in the cabin during bad weather.
  D learning to move about in a certain way.

3 When Clyde talks about the biggest danger he's faced he
  A corrects a misconception about solo sailing.
  B gives the example of one dangerous storm.
  C argues that the ocean is as dangerous as it ever was.
  D admits that ocean sailing was more dangerous than he'd expected.

4 What has been the main cause of Clyde falling sick during his sailing experiences?
  A tropical diseases
  B contact with land
  C food poisoning
  D monotonous diet

5 How does Clyde describe the fear he's experienced at sea?
  A There have been occasional times of great terror.
  B His experiences of fear have diminished over time.
  C He experiences constant low-level anxiety at sea.
  D As he gets older he feels afraid more often.

6 Clyde says that the most special times of a voyage are
  A losing sight of land.
  B sunrise and sunset.
  C the night time.
  D the first sight of land.

3 This is the modern world

Multiple matching **1.16–1.20**

You will hear five short extracts in which people talk about an experiment in which they were not allowed to use any modern technology for one week.

While you listen you must complete both tasks.

TASK ONE

For questions **1–5**, choose from the list (**A–H**) what aspect of each speaker's life was most affected by the experiment.

A taking photographs

B reading e-books

C keeping up with current affairs

D playing games

E keeping in touch with clients

F doing research

G keeping in touch with friends

H making bookings

Speaker 1	1
Speaker 2	2
Speaker 3	3
Speaker 4	4
Speaker 5	5

TASK TWO

For questions **6–10**, choose from the list (**A–H**) how the experiment made each person feel.

A regretful about taking part

B bored while commuting

C jealous of workmates

D frustrated that others were not sympathetic

E angry to be so technology-dependent

F anxious about former colleagues

G stressed about family members

H disappointed in himself/herself

Speaker 1	6
Speaker 2	7
Speaker 3	8
Speaker 4	9
Speaker 5	10

9 Going places

Listening
Part 3

Multiple choice **1.21**

You will hear an interview with a British woman called Jenny Parker, who recently travelled to the country of Vanuatu, a group of islands in the South Pacific, as part of her gap year. For questions **1–6**, choose the answer (**A**, **B**, **C** or **D**) which fits best according to what you hear.

1 Jenny decided to go to Vanuatu because she wanted to
   A travel in an inexpensive country.
   B experience something totally new.
   C visit someone she had met travelling.
   D escape from work she found dull.

2 What was Jenny's first reaction to the capital, Port Vila?
   A The friendliness of the people surprised her.
   B She was relieved by the pleasant climate.
   C The range of food available was limited.
   D She was impressed by the contrasting sights.

3 What did Jenny find unexpected about Tanna Island?
   A The condition of the island's roads.
   B The difficulties of climbing the volcano.
   C The importance of magic to the islanders.
   D The volcanic eruptions visible at night time.

4 Jenny describes her experience on the 'Nakamal' in order to
   A correct a misconception about traditional cultures.
   B highlight an aspect of the culture she found challenging.
   C compare Vanuatu's culture to other neighbouring countries.
   D illustrate the cultural diversity of the country.

5 When Jenny talks about diving at Million Dollar Point she is
   A critical of the way equipment had been wasted.
   B worried the site has been degraded over time.
   C concerned about future damage to the environment.
   D disappointed by the attitudes shown by other divers.

6 What point does Jenny make about the local pidgin English, 'Bislama'?
   A It's difficult for an outsider to learn.
   B It's an entertaining insight into the islands.
   C Its origins are not clearly understood.
   D The people are pleased if visitors can speak it.

10 House and home

Listening
Part 4

Multiple matching  **1.22–1.26**

You will hear five short extracts in which people talk about a home they have lived in at some time in the past.

While you listen you must complete both tasks.

TASK ONE

For questions **1–5**, choose from the list (**A–H**) what type of home it was.

A   a top floor apartment
B   a suburban house
C   a caravan
D   a farm house
E   a beach house
F   a boat
G   a basement apartment
H   a mountain chalet

Speaker 1	**1**
Speaker 2	**2**
Speaker 3	**3**
Speaker 4	**4**
Speaker 5	**5**

TASK TWO

For questions **6–10**, choose from the list (**A–H**) what aspect of the home each speaker liked.

A   it had a good kitchen.
B   it was conveniently situated
C   it was quiet
D   it was affordable
E   it had good views
F   it gave a sense of security
G   it was spacious
H   it was private

Speaker 1	**6**
Speaker 2	**7**
Speaker 3	**8**
Speaker 4	**9**
Speaker 5	**10**

11 A cultural education

Listening
Part 1

Multiple choice **1.27–1.29**

You will hear three different extracts. For questions **1–6**, choose the answer (**A**, **B** or **C**) which fits best according to what you hear. There are two questions for each extract.

Extract 1

You hear two university students talking about a new current affairs show on television.

1 What aspect of the show does the woman like?

  A There are three presenters.

  B It is longer than its predecessor.

  C There is a mix of local and international stories.

2 Both speakers believe that the show is

  A intended for an older audience.

  B unlikely to last very long.

  C based on another TV show.

Extract 2

You hear two fans of the football club City talking about tonight's match against United.

3 The man thinks that United

  A will be nervous about such a big game.

  B have too many injured players at present.

  C will be unprepared for their opponent's tactics.

4 The woman thinks that City

  A will win if the forecast rain arrives.

  B have not prepared for the game in the best way.

  C wants this win more than their opponent does.

Extract 3

You hear a woman and a man who run a corner shop talking about the business.

5 What concern does the woman have for the future of the business?

  A the ageing population

  B the effects of technology

  C the competition from larger shops

6 Both speakers agree that the best thing about running a corner shop is

  A having contact with regular customers.

  B being at the centre of the community.

  C knowing so many local children.

12 The world about us

Listening
Part 2

Sentence completion **1.30**

You hear a student called Jason Brown giving a talk about a day he spent as a volunteer working to restore the ecology of Franklin Island. For questions **1–8**, complete the sentences with a word or short phrase.

Restoring the Ecology of Franklin Island

Jason explains that the island used to be a **(1)** .... belonging to the Franklins.

Jason approves of the way that large numbers of **(2)** .... were established on the island in 2005.

In Jason's opinion, the worst threat to the island's birds were pests such as

(3) .... that hunted them.

Jason spent the morning helping to expand the network of **(4)** .... on the island.

In the afternoon Jason helped remove **(5)** .... , some of which were very old.

Working in the **(6)** .... will appeal to people who don't want hard physical work.

Volunteers are currently counting the species of **(7)** .... *and* .... on the island.

Later in the year there will be a day to collect **(8)** .... to help maintain the island's ecology.

13 Food for thought

Multiple choice **1.31–1.33**

You will hear three different extracts. For questions **1–6**, choose the answer (**A**, **B** or **C**) which fits best according to what you hear. There are two questions for each extract.

Extract 1

You hear two university students talking about the cafeteria in their hall of residence.

1 What aspect of the cafeteria has surprised the woman?

   A the wide range of food available

   B the variable quality of meals

   C the flexible hours of service

2 The man sometimes does not eat in their hall of residence because

   A he cannot afford it.

   B his friends eat elsewhere.

   C he does not like the food.

Extract 2

You hear two friends talking about going on a camping holiday.

3 What concern does the man have about their equipment?

   A They still do not have some equipment.

   B Some of their equipment is poor quality.

   C They do not know what equipment to take.

4 Both speakers agree that the camping holiday

   A would have benefited from more planning.

   B may be their last holiday together of this kind.

   C was a good compromise under the circumstances.

Extract 3

You hear two university students talking about a new lecturer on their course.

5 The woman likes the new tutor because

   A he seems very young and energetic.

   B he is quite flexible about deadlines.

   C he has an unconventional background.

6 What does the man say about the new tutor?

   A He might be disorganized.

   B He could be divisive.

   C He may be inexperienced.

14 Money matters

Listening
Part 3

Multiple choice 1.34

You will hear an interview with a man called Jim Barnes who has recovered gold from an old shipwreck. For questions **1–6**, choose the answer (**A**, **B**, **C** or **D**) which fits best according to what you hear.

1 When did Jim realize he might have found the site of a sunken ship?

  A He saw an unusual shape.

  B Documents revealed a shipwreck.

  C He saw a shiny object on the seabed.

  D A team member discovered an artefact.

2 Jim did not return to the site of the shipwreck for five years because he had to

  A raise funds.

  B obtain permission.

  C assemble the equipment.

  D complete other projects.

3 According to Jim, the *Lyttleton Star* probably sank because

  A the weather was unexpectedly bad.

  B the captain made a navigational error.

  C the ship was poorly designed.

  D the crew were too few in number.

4 How did Jim feel on the voyage back to the Kermadec Islands?

  A He was nervous that the expedition might find nothing of value.

  B Discovering the identity of the ship had become an obsession.

  C The thought of becoming rich made him very excited.

  D He wanted to prove a prominent historian wrong.

5 After the first week of diving Jim was

  A surprised the condition of the ship was so bad.

  B disappointed by the performance of the equipment.

  C frustrated that the layout of the ship was not clear.

  D anxious about the health of an expedition member.

6 What impressed Jim most when he first saw the gold?

  A the quality of the metal

  B the location of the find

  C the number of bars

  D the reaction of the team

Word formation list

Nouns

-age

Verb	Noun
break	breakage
cover	coverage
pack	package
post	postage
store	storage
wreck	wreckage

Adjective	Noun
short	shortage

-al

Verb	Noun
(dis)approve	(dis)approval
arrive	arrival
bury	burial
deny	denial
dismiss	dismissal
propose	proposal
rehearse	rehearsal
remove	removal
renew	renewal
revive	revival
survive	survival

-ance

Verb	Noun
annoy	annoyance
(dis)appear	(dis)appearance
attend	attendance
disturb	disturbance
endure	endurance
enter	entrance
ignore	ignorance
inherit	inheritance
perform	performance
rely	reliance
resemble	resemblance
resist	resistance
signify	(in)significance
tolerate	(in)tolerance

Adjective	Noun
arrogant	arrogance
distant	distance
(un)important	(un)importance
(ir)relevant	(ir)relevance
reluctant	reluctance

-ence

Verb	Noun
confide	confidence
depend	(in)dependence
differ	difference
exist	existence
insist	insistence
obey	obedience
occur	occurrence
offend	offence
persist	persistence
recur	recurrence

Adjective	Noun
absent	absence
(in)competent	(in)competence
(in)convenient	(in)convenience
evident	evidence
innocent	innocence
intelligent	intelligence
(im)patient	(im)patience
present	presence
violent	violence

-cy

Adjective	Noun
(in)accurate	(in)accuracy
(in)adequate	(in)adequacy
bankrupt	bankruptcy
(in)decent	(in)decency
(in)efficient	(in)efficiency
(in)frequent	(in)frequency
immediate	immediacy
infant	infancy
intimate	intimacy
(il)literate	(il)literacy
pregnant	pregnancy
private	privacy
proficient	proficiency
redundant	redundancy
secret	secrecy
urgent	urgency
vacant	vacancy

Noun	Noun
pirate	piracy

-dom

Adjective	Noun
bored	boredom
free	freedom

wise	wisdom

Person	Abstract noun
king	kingdom
star	stardom

-ful

Noun	Noun (Quantity)
arm	armful
cup	cupful
fist	fistful
hand	handful
house	houseful
room	roomful
spoon	spoonful

-hood

Person	Abstract noun
adult	adulthood
child	childhood
father	fatherhood
man	manhood
mother	motherhood
neighbour	neighbourhood*
parent	parenthood
woman	womanhood

*neighbourhood
part of a town or city where people live

Adjective	Noun
likely	likelihood

-iety

Adjective	Noun
anxious	anxiety
notorious	notoriety
sober	sobriety
various	variety

-ity

Adjective	Noun
(un)able	(in)ability
(in)active	(in)activity
complex	complexity
credible	credibility
curious	curiosity
(un)equal	(in)equality
(un)familiar	(un)familiarity
ferocious	ferocity
(in)flexible	(in)flexibility
(in)formal	(in)formality

generous	generosity
hostile	hostility
immune	immunity
intense	intensity
major	majority
minor	minority
(im)mobile	(im)mobility
objective	objectivity
(un)original	(un)originality
personal	personality
(un)popular	(un)popularity
prosperous	prosperity
(im)pure	(im)purity
(in)secure	(in)security
(in)sensitive	(in)sensitivity
severe	severity
similar	similarity
simple	simplicity
(in)sincere	(in)sincerity
stupid	stupidity
subjective	subjectivity
(in)valid	(in)validity

-ing

Verb	Noun
advertise	advertising
build	building
gather	gathering
like	liking
live	living
meet	meeting
record	recording
say	saying
set	setting
suffer	suffering

-ment

Verb	Noun
achieve	achievement
(dis)agree	(dis)agreement
amaze	amazement
amuse	amusement
announce	announcement
argue	argument
arrange	arrangement
commit	commitment
content	contentment
develop	development
disappoint	disappointment
discourage	discouragement
embarrass	embarrassment
employ	(un)employment
encourage	encouragement
enjoy	enjoyment

entertain	entertainment
excite	excitement
govern	government
improve	improvement
invest	investment
involve	involvement
judge	judgement/
judgment	
manage	management
measure	measurement
move	movement
(re)pay	(re)payment
punish	punishment
refresh	refreshment
replace	replacement
require	requirement
retire	retirement
settle	settlement
treat	treatment

-ness

Adjective	Noun
(un)aware	(un)awareness
careless	carelessness
close	closeness
(un)conscious	(un)consciousness
deaf	deafness
eager	eagerness
(in)effective	(in)effectiveness
(un)friendly	(un)friendliness
great	greatness
hard	hardness
hopeless	hopelessness
(un)selfish	(un)selfishness
serious	seriousness
stiff	stiffness
thorough	thoroughness
tired	tiredness
useful	usefulness
weak	weakness

-ship

Person	Abstract noun
champion	championship
companion	companionship
friend	friendship
leader	leadership
member	membership
owner	ownership
partner	partnership
scholar	scholarship*
sponsor	sponsorship**

*scholarship
money given to someone to help pay for their studies
**sponsorship
money given to someone/an organization to help pay for something, e.g. an event

Adjective	Noun
hard	hardship

-sis

Verb	Noun
analyse	analysis
base	basis
diagnose	diagnosis
emphasize	emphasis

-sion

Verb	Noun
collide	collision
comprehend	comprehension
conclude	conclusion
confuse	confusion
convert	conversion
decide	decision
divert	diversion
divide	division
erode	erosion
evade	evasion
exclude	exclusion
expand	expansion
explode	explosion
include	inclusion
intrude	intrusion
invade	invasion
persuade	persuasion
supervise	supervision

-son

Verb	Noun
compare	comparison

-ation

Verb	Noun
adapt	adaptation
administer	administration
apply	application
combine	combination
compile	compilation
consider	consideration
expect	expectation
explain	explanation
identify	identification
imagine	imagination
inflame	inflammation
inform	information

Word formation list

inspire	inspiration
interpret	interpretation
observe	observation
prepare	preparation
present	presentation
publish	publication
(dis)qualify	(dis)qualification
realize	realization
resign	resignation
vary	variation

-tion

Verb	Noun
accommodate	accommodation
(re)act	(re)action
associate	association
collect	collection
complicate	complication
compose	composition
(dis)connect	(dis)connection
contaminate	contamination
demonstrate	demonstration
direct	direction
evolve	evolution
hesitate	hesitation
imitate	imitation
inhibit	inhibition
investigate	investigation
(de)motivate	(de)motivation
operate	operation
perceive	perception
predict	prediction
prescribe	prescription
receive	reception
recognize	recognition
reduce	reduction
repeat	repetition
(dis)satisfy	(dis)satisfaction
(re)solve	(re)solution
subscribe	subscription
substitute	substitution

-th

Adjective	Noun
broad	breadth
deep	depth
long	length
strong	strength
true	truth
warm	warmth
wide	width
young	youth

Verb	Noun
grow	growth

-ure

Verb	Noun
close	closure
compose	composure
depart	departure
expose	exposure
fail	failure
please	pleasure
proceed	procedure
sign	signature

-y

Adjective	Noun
difficult	difficulty
(dis)honest	(dis)honesty
poor	poverty
safe	safety
(un)certain	(un)certainty

Verb	Noun
discover	discovery
enter	entry

People

-ant

Verb	Person
apply	applicant
assist	assistant
confide	confidant(e)
consult	consultant
contest	contestant
defend	defendant
inhabit	inhabitant
occupy	occupant
participate	participant

-ar

Verb	Person
lie	liar

-ative

Verb	Person
represent	representative

-er

Verb	Person
employ	employer
lecture	lecturer
manufacture	manufacturer
present	presenter
read	reader
research	researcher
win	winner

-ian

Noun	Person
comedy	comedian
electricity	electrician
history	historian
library	librarian
mathematics	mathematician
music	musician
politics	politician

-ist

Noun	Person
bicycle	cyclist
environment	environmentalist
motor (car)	motorist
nature	naturalist
novel	novelist
psychiatry	psychiatrist
science	scientist
specialism	specialist
violin	violinist

-or

Verb	Person
act	actor
collect	collector
communicate	communicator
compete	competitor
conduct	conductor
contribute	contributor
demonstrate	demonstrator
distribute	distributor
instruct	instructor
invent	inventor
spectate	spectator

Nouns formed with up, down, in, away, out, back

up-	in-
upbringing	income
upkeep	input
uprising	insight
uproar	intake
upset	
upturn	

-away

getaway
hideaway
runaway
takeaway

down-

downfall
downpour
downside
downturn

-down

breakdown

out-

outbreak
outburst
outcome
outline
outlook
output
outset

-out

breakout
checkout
handout

knockout
lookout
payout
turnout
workout

-back

comeback
drawback
feedback
setback

back-

background

Miscellaneous

Verb	Noun
(mis)behave	(mis)behaviour
choose	choice
complain	complaint
die	death
give	gift
know	knowledge
laugh	laughter
lose	loss
prove	proof
receive	receipt
respond	response

Verb	Noun
sell	sale(s)
succeed	success
think	thought
try	trial
weigh	weight

Adjective	Noun
high	height

Adjectives

-able

Verb	Adjective
accept	(un)acceptable
advise	(in)advisable
afford	affordable
agree	(dis)agreeable
apply	(in)applicable
appreciate	appreciable
approach	(un)approachable
avoid	(un)avoidable
bear	(un)bearable
believe	(un)believable
compare	(in)comparable
consider	(in)considerable
desire	(un)desirable

dispense	(in)dispensable
forget	(un)forgettable
imagine	(un)imaginable
irritate	irritable
note	notable
notice	noticeable
pay	payable
predict	(un)predictable
prefer	preferable
prevent	preventable
regret	regrettable
rely	(un)reliable
remark	(un)remarkable
respect	respectable
understand	understandable
work	(un)workable

Noun	Adjective
comfort	(un)comfortable
fashion	(un)fashionable
knowledge	knowledgeable
memory	(un)memorable
profit	(un)profitable
reason	(un)reasonable
value	(in)valuable

-ible

Noun	Adjective
access	(in)accessible
flexibility	(in)flexible
sense	(in)sensible*

Verb	Adjective
comprehend	(in)comprehensible
defend	(in)defensible
perceive	(im)perceptible
resist	(ir)resistible
respond	(ir)responsible
reverse	(ir)reversible

* sensible:

showing or having good sense, e.g. *Cycling with a broken arm is not a very sensible thing to do.*

insensible:

a unconscious
e.g. *He was found drunk and insensible.*

b not caring about or unaware of
e.g. *She seemed insensible to the dangers involved.*

-al

Noun	Adjective
accident	accidental
addition	additional
alphabet	alphabetical

behaviour	behavioural
centre	central
culture	cultural
ecology	ecological
emotion	(un)emotional
environment	environmental
exception	(un)exceptional
experiment	experimental
fact	factual
globe	global
intention	intentional
medicine	medicinal
method	methodical
monument	monumental
nation	national
occasion	occasional
occupation	occupational
origin	(un)original
parent	parental
person	(im)personal
practice	(im)practical
profession	(un)professional
sensation	(un)sensational
society	social
temperament	temperamental
tradition	traditional
universe	universal

-ial

Noun	Adjective
benefit	beneficial
commerce	commercial
controversy	(un)controversial
face	facial
finance	financial
industry	industrial
influence	influential
manager	managerial
matrimony	matrimonial
residence	residential
secretary	secretarial
substance	(in)substantial
territory	territorial

-ant

Verb	Adjective
ignore	ignorant
please	(un)pleasant
rely	reliant
resist	resistant
signify	(in)significant
tolerate	(in)tolerant

Word formation list

-ent

Verb	Adjective
appear	apparent
confide	confident
depend	(in)dependent
insist	insistent
obey	(dis)obedient
persist	persistent
recur	recurrent

Noun	Adjective
absence	absent
(in)competence	(in)competent
(in)convenience	(in)convenient
evidence	evident
(in)frequency	(in)frequent
innocence	innocent
intelligence	intelligent
(im)patience	(im)patient
presence	present

-ate

Noun	Adjective
accuracy	(in)accurate
adequacy	(in)adequate
appropriacy	(in)appropriate
consideration	(in)considerate
fortune	(un)fortunate
moderation	(im)moderate

-ative

Verb	Adjective
administer	administrative
argue	argumentative
compare	comparative
consult	consultative
imagine	(un)imaginative
inform	(un)informative
prevent	preventative
provoke	provocative
represent	(un)representative

-ive

Verb	Adjective
act	(in)active
adopt	adoptive
appreciate	(un)appreciative
assert	(un)assertive
attend	(in)attentive
attract	(un)attractive
communicate	(un)communicative
compete	(un)competitive
conclude	(in)conclusive
construct	(un)constructive
cooperate	(un)cooperative
create	(un)creative
deceive	deceptive
decide	(in)decisive
defend	defensive
describe	descriptive
destroy	destructive
disrupt	disruptive
divide	divisive
explode	explosive
express	expressive
extend	extensive
impress	(un)impressive
include	inclusive
invent	inventive
offend	(in)offensive
persuade	persuasive
possess	possessive
produce	(un)productive
progress	progressive
protect	protective
receive	(un)receptive
respect	(ir)respective
respond	(un)responsive
speculate	speculative
support	(un)supportive

Noun	Adjective
aggression	(un)aggressive
effect	(in)effective
expense	(in)expensive
secret	secretive
sense	(in)sensitive

-ing/-ed

The following verbs can be used to form participle adjectives

e.g. *worrying/worried*

alarm, amaze, amuse, annoy, astonish, bore, confuse, convince, depress, disappoint, disgust, embarrass, entertain, excite, exhaust, fascinate, frighten, frustrate, increase, interest, irritate, motivate, move, refresh, relax, satisfy, shock, surprise, terrify, threaten, thrill, tire, worry

The following *-ing* adjectives are commonly used with the nouns in brackets.

Verb	Adjective
close	closing (date)
consult	consulting (room)
recur	recurring (illness, nightmare, problem, theme)
run	running (water)
support	supporting (actor, actress, evidence, role)

-ous

Noun	Adjective
(dis)advantage	(dis)advantageous
ambition	(un)ambitious
anxiety	anxious
caution	cautious
courtesy	(dis)courteous
curiosity	curious
danger	dangerous
disaster	disastrous
glamour	(un)glamorous
hazard	hazardous
humour	humorous
luxury	luxurious
monster	monstrous
mystery	mysterious
nerve	nervous
number	numerous
poison	poisonous
religion	(ir)religious
suspicion	suspicious

Verb	Adjective
infect	infectious
vary	various

-ly

Noun	Adjective
friend	(un)friendly
life	lively
time	(un)timely

-y

Noun	Adjective
chat	chatty
cloud	cloudy
ease	easy
fault	faulty
fog	foggy
frost	frosty
grass	grassy
guilt	guilty
hair	hairy
hill	hilly
mist	misty
mud	muddy
rain	rainy
rock	rocky
sleep	sleepy
sun	sunny
wealth	wealthy

-ful/-less

Root	-ful	-less/un__ful
beauty	beautiful	————
care	careful	careless
cheer	cheerful	cheerless*
colour	colourful	colourless
count	————	countless
deceit	deceitful	————
delight	delightful	————
effort	————	effortless
end	————	endless
event	eventful	uneventful
faith	faithful	unfaithful
fault	faulty	faultless
flight	————	flightless
gratitude	grateful	ungrateful
hair	hairy	hairless
harm	harmful	harmless
heart	————	heartless
help	helpful	helpless*/ unhelpful*
home	————	homeless
hope	hopeful	hopeless
hurt	hurtful	————
job	————	jobless
meaning	meaningful	meaningless
pain	painful	painless
peace	peaceful	————
point	————	pointless
power	powerful	powerless
price	————	priceless*
relent	————	relentless
resource	resourceful	unresourceful
respect	respectful	disrespectful
skill	skilful*/skilled*	unskilled
sleep	————	sleepless
speech	————	speechless
stress	stressful	unstressful
success	successful	unsuccessful
taste	tasty*/tasteful*	tasteless
thought	thoughtful*	thoughtless
time	————	timeless
truth	truthful	untruthful
use	useful	useless
waste	wasteful	————
wonder	wonderful	————
worth	————	worthless*
youth	youthful	————

cheerless: used mainly to describe the weather or a room which is not bright or pleasant

helpless: unable to do anything to help or protect yourself

unhelpful: not willing to help other people

priceless: used to describe an object which has a very high value; it is worth so much money that the price cannot be calculated (compare with *worthless* below)

skilful/skilled: both can be used to describe a person who has the necessary ability, experience and/or training to do something well.

e.g. *He's a skilful footballer. This work was done by skilled craftsmen.*

skilled: can also be used to describe a job or piece of work that requires special skill and training

e.g. *Nursing is a skilled job.*

tasty: used to describe food with a strong and pleasant flavour

tasteful: used to describe clothes, decoration, etc which is attractive and shows good taste

thoughtful:

a to describe a person who is quiet and serious because they are thinking about something

b to describe someone who thinks and cares about the feelings and needs of other people

worthless: used to describe an object with no value in money (compare with *priceless* above)

-ic

Noun	Adjective
allergy	allergic
drama	dramatic
optimism	optimistic
pessimism	pessimistic
science	scientific
strategy	strategic

-ary

Noun	Adjective
caution	cautionary
literature	literary
revolution	revolutionary
Verb	**Adjective**
imagine	imaginary
volunteer	(in)voluntary

Word formation list

-ory

Verb	Adjective
advise	advisory
celebrate	celebratory
contradict	contradictory
explain	explanatory
introduce	introductory
migrate	migratory
oblige	obligatory
prepare	preparatory
satisfy	(un)satisfactory
supervise	supervisory

Verbs

-ate

Noun	Verb
alien	alienate
assassin	assassinate
difference	differentiate
value	evaluate

Adjective	Verb
active	activate
captive	captivate
dominant	dominate
valid	validate

en-

Noun	Verb
act	enact
circle	encircle
courage	encourage (discourage)
danger	endanger
force	enforce
list	enlist
rage	enrage
trust	entrust

Adjective	Verb
able	enable
large	enlarge
rich	enrich
sure	ensure

-ify

Noun	Verb
class	classify
example	exemplify
glory	glorify
identity	identify
note	notify
(dis)qualification	(dis)qualify

Adjective	Verb
clear	clarify
just	justify
pure	purify
simple	simplify
solid	solidify

-en

Adjective	Verb
black	blacken
bright	brighten
broad	broaden
dark	darken
dead	deaden
deaf	deafen
deep	deepen
fat	fatten
flat	flatten
fresh	freshen
hard	harden
high	heighten
light	lighten
long	lengthen
less	lessen
loose	loosen
moist	moisten
quick	quicken
red	redden
ripe	ripen
sad	sadden
sharp	sharpen
short	shorten
soft	soften
stiff	stiffen
straight	straighten
strong	strengthen
sweet	sweeten
thick	thicken
tight	tighten
weak	weaken
wide	widen
worse	worsen

Noun	Verb
threat	threaten

-ize

Noun	Verb
character	characterize
climate	acclimatize
computer	computerize
criticism	criticize
emphasis	emphasize
maximum	maximize
memory	memorize
minimum	minimize
moisture	moisturize
pressure	pressurize
revolution	revolutionize
standard	standardize
summary	summarize
symbol	symbolize
sympathy	sympathize

Adjective	Verb
commercial	commercialize
familiar	familiarize
formal	formalize
general	generalize
item	itemize
modern	modernize
social	socialize
special	specialize
stable	stabilize
visual	visualize

Verbs formed with up, down, over, under, out

up-	down-
update	downgrade
upgrade	download
uphold	downplay
uplift	downshift
uproot	downsize
upset	
upstage	

over-	under-
overcome	underachieve
overcook	undercharge
overeat	undercut
overestimate	underestimate
overexpose	undergo
overflow	underline
overhear	underrate
overheat	understate
overload	undertake
overlook	undervalue
overrate	

out-
outgrow
outlast
outlive
outnumber
outplay
outrun
outstay

over-
overrule
overrun
overshadow
oversleep
overspend
overstay
overstretch
overtake
overthrow
overuse
overwork

Answer key

Unit 1

Reading and Use of English, page 4

Part 8 Multiple matching

1

B

2

1 C	2 A	3 D	4 B	5 D
6 A	7 B	8 C	9 D	10 B

Vocabulary, page 6

A Verb and noun collocations

1 into 2 with 3 out 4 in 5 to

B Adjective and noun collocations

1

1 inside 2 resounding 3 burning 4 hard
5 terrible 6 urgent 7 heated 8 outlying

2

1 slim 2 recurrent 3 daunting 4 poor 5 overnight
6 dismal 7 lifelong 8 sporting

C Word formation

1 exposure 2 proposals 3 inflexibility 4 vacancies
5 emphasis 6 requirements 7 closeness 8 shortage
9 irrelevance 10 notoriety

Language focus, page 7

A Spelling

Incorrect spelling	Correct spelling
writting	writing
apeared	appeared
Loosers	Losers
wich	which
agressive	aggressive
wellfare	welfare
totaly	totally
although	although
their	there
ougth	ought
adition	addition
intervue	interview
where	were
oportunity	opportunity
impresive	impressive
pane	pain
too	to
extremly	extremely
innacuracies	inaccuracies
faithfuly	faithfully

B Modal verbs: *might, could, may* **and** *can*

1

1 live here, but we never see him
2 (very) well be asked to speak French during the interview
3 not have known you were married
4 (well) have got it
5 as well sell it
6 have told me you were vegetarian
7 have been enjoying herself very much

2

1 can 2 could 3 may 4 could 5 may 6 could
7 could

Reading and Use of English, page 9

Part 1 Multiple-choice cloze

1 C	2 B	3 A	4 C	5 D
6 D	7 A	8 B		

Writing, page 10

Part 2 Formal letter: application

1

Suggested answers:

possess good communication skills, be well-organized, have relevant experience, an eye for detail, an ability to work well under pressure, an ability to work to deadlines, an ability to use your initiative, be dynamic, of smart appearance, versatile, etc

2

The following are incorrect:

1 apply 2 must 3 enveloped 4 destined 5 place
6 number 7 chores 8 conduct 9 sorting 10 learnt
11 rise for 12 own 13 complete 14 welcome
15 actual

3

How to go about it:

Paragraph organization in Lara Goodrich's letter

1 reasons for writing
2 relevant experience
3 reasons for applying, suitability for job
4 availability
5 closing comment

Unit 2

Reading and Use of English, page 12

Part 5 Multiple choice

1 D	2 B	3 C	4 A	5 B	6 D

Answer key

Vocabulary, page 14

Changes

1

1 transferred **2** shifted **3** adapted **4** altered

2

1 B **2** D **3** A **4** C **5** A

3

1 scene **2** heart **3** pace **4** direction **5** fortunes
6 condition **7** law **8** attitudes

Language focus, page 15

1

1 used to **2** was (still) eating **3** met **4** have eaten
5 have seen/saw **6** had caught **7** have stayed
8 hadn't given **9** have done **10** to sit

2

A

1 has been putting **2** has managed **3** has met
4 believed/used to believe **5** asked/used to ask/would
ask **6** have changed **7** said **8** lit/used to light/
would light

B

1 went **2** saw/had seen **3** was working/worked
4 booked/had booked **5** Having washed **6** had just
landed **7** had been experiencing **8** would take/was
going to take **9** spent **10** didn't arrive **11** had been
sitting **12** had left/would be leaving/was going to
leave/was leaving **13** had ever had **14** would be/was
going to be

Reading and Use of English, page 16

Part 2 Open cloze

1 nowhere **2** should **3** which **4** went **5** with
6 as **7** what **8** however/though

Part 3 Word formation

1 beautifully **2** adaptation **3** dissatisfaction
4 starring **5** sales **6** variation **7** discovery
8 threatens

Part 4 Key word transformation

1 have warned/told you not to **2** didn't use to like/
enjoy **3** would like to have carried/gone **4** like to
express my dissatisfaction **5** would sooner have
stayed **6** you rather I hadn't let

Writing, page 18

Part 2 Formal and informal letter

2

1 satisfaction **2** deal **3** knowledge
4 explanations **5** attention **6** improve **7** Firstly
8 departure **9** failed **10** addition **11** illness
12 Finally **13** discover/learn/hear **14** arrival
15 entrance/admission

Unit 3

Reading and Use of English, page 20

Part 7 Gapped text

1 E **2** A **3** B **4** C **5** F **6** D
G = not used

Vocabulary, page 22

A Adjective and noun collocations

1

Across: **3** ambition **5** aroma **6** method **8** success
11 change **12** challenge
Down: **1** changes **2** odour **4** information **7** failure
9 chance **10** smell

2 *Possible answers*
(see also Wordlist on pages 208–209 of the Coursebook)

lifelong/secret **ambition**
pleasant/sweet **aroma**
convenient/efficient **method**
huge/great **success**
refreshing/pleasant **change**
formidable/major **challenge**
far-reaching/significant **changes**
acrid/stale **odour**
biased/reliable **information**
total/continued **failure**
slight/remote **chance**
faint/rancid **smell**

B Verb and noun collocations

1

1 an ambition **2** information **3** a challenge
4 change **5** a problem **6** a possibility **7** a smell

2

1 pursue **2** gathering **3** presents **4** resisting
5 resolved **6** looking into **7** get rid of

C Word formation

1 ignorant **2** countless **3** inaccessible **4** numerous
5 surprisingly **6** literary **7** unsuccessful **8**
comparative **9** dramatically **10** introductory

Language focus, page 24

1

1 had seen/watched **2** rather/sooner have **3** been
for **4** have worn/taken **5** to have **6** Had I
7 you had, would/could have **8** might/would not/
never, been driving/travelling/going

2

1 C **2** A, B, C **3** B **4** A, B, C **5** A, B **6** B, C **7** C
8 A, C

Reading and Use of English, page 25

Part 1 Multiple-choice cloze
1 D   **2** C   **3** C   **4** B   **5** D
6 A   **7** C   **8** C

Part 2 Open cloze
1 go **2** even **3** It **4** Having **5** to **6** with
7 However **8** took

Writing, page 26

Part 2 Review
2

para 1: grab reader's attention; introduce the performance for review

para 2: give background to present performance

para 3: brief summary of plot; positive opinions of performance

para 4: minor criticism; concluding opinions; recommendation

3

The writer immediately picks out a point of interest: a large number of young performers; and creates some sense of anticipation – will it result in a bad show? The writer then provides a picture of the stage filled with skilful dancers and of the audience's attention being captured.

4

varied performances, unique meeting place, straightforward, comic, spellbinding, moving, particularly accomplished, enormously impressive, inadequate resources, unavoidable limitations

5

1 debut **2** timing **3** acoustics **4** casting **5** success
6 leads **7** repertoire **8** interpretation

Unit 4

Reading and Use of English, page 28

Part 6 Cross-text multiple matching
1 B

B *Essentially, it was my decision to tolerate the circumstances.*

C *In retrospect, I see how this ridiculous situation was self-inflicted – a result of my need for perfection.*

2 A

A *I would like to write a piece about the wisdom gained following my disillusionment with my work, but that would be fictitious.*

B *This gave me the opportunity to take stock and see how I could combine my passion for music with a new career.*

C *I took a sabbatical and finally had the mental space to reassess my priorities and myself: whereas I once regarded my obsessive qualities as a professional advantage, since then, I have made a conscious effort to suppress them.*

D *Indeed, realizing my own limitations was a sharp learning curve; it helped me redress the balance I needed in life and identify new priorities.*

3 C

A *I expected my employers to be sympathetic but I was, in essence, given an ultimatum; get back to work or move on, and it was this attitude that has left a bitter taste.*

C *At the same time, I resent the fact that my superiors were well aware of my level of fatigue and anxiety and did nothing to alleviate it. You know then that you are a mere cog in the machine.*

4 D

A *Anecdotal evidence suggests mine was hardly a unique case, …*

B *It was physically and emotionally draining but that's the nature of the executive lifestyle …*

C *That desperate phenomenon of being 'used up' by years of corporate servitude is something I knew was prevalent but never contemplated happening to me.*

D *I feel that industry in general has come a long way in terms of employee welfare; there was a time when you got the sense that executives were being driven to the point of collapse, but corporate ethos appears to have changed since then.*

Verb + noun collocations
1/2

1 taste **2** potential **3** notice **4** grudge **5** credit
6 effort **7** qualms **8** way

Compound nouns

1 performance, management **2** career **3** pay
4 learning

Vocabulary, page 30

A Body idioms

1 nose, head **2** foot, eye, eye **3** brains, head **4** feet, head **5** face, knees

2

1 c, h **2** b, f **3** j, a **4** i, d **5** g, e

B Time

1 for **2** out **3** aside **4** up **5** of **6** in **7** at **8** to
9 on **10** off

Language focus, page 31

A Gerunds and infinitives

1 refusal to work overtime surprised me.

2 isn't worth (you/your) reading that book.

3 you like me to carry your bag for you?

4 made a big/great/every effort to give up junk food.

5 appreciate you/your coming at such short notice.

6 couldn't help laughing when he said that.

7 had better leave now if you don't want to miss/or you'll miss the bus.

8 have difficulty remembering names.

9 were made to clean up the mess.

10 to him/his being treated so badly.

B Punctuation

1 Since employees **2** night, profits **3** doubled.
4 nights **5** director, went **6** explained that
7 'Often **8** Mistry, **9** accounts department
10 women. **11** don't **12** other's **13** It's
14 years, said **15** However, **16** now,' he confessed.

Reading and Use of English, page 32

Part 1 Multiple-choice cloze

1 D **2** A **3** C **4** B **5** A **6** B **7** D **8** B

Part 2 Open cloze

1 to **2** although/though/while/whilst/whereas **3** of
4 at **5** once **6** is **7** on **8** not

Part 3 Word formation

1 representatives **2** determination **3** leadership
4 attendance **5** applicants **6** preferred/preferable
7 competitive **8** receipt

Writing, page 34

Part 2 Reports

2

The correct order and possible headings are:

4 Introduction **2** General background **1** The effect
of the car **5** The effect of television **3** Future
developments

3

Language used to compare the past and the present:

Street games … are no longer such a common sight.

cycling … is becoming less attractive

youngsters now spend more time in the home …

The main difference between now and twenty years
ago …

the increased wealth and greater amount of free time
available …

Where previously whole families … , now children …

Courting couples rarely go ballroom dancing … as
they once did; instead …

Language used to make future predictions:

Teenagers and people in their twenties may well
spend …

They might even begin to wish …

Different ways of referring to young people:

young people, our youth, teenagers and people in
their twenties, children, courting couples

Different ways of referring to free time:

free time, spare time, leisure time

4

*but two other developments have restricted the nature
and quality of leisure time activities*

Sadly, youngsters now spend more time in the home

*they stay in to watch television, or perhaps worse,
attend wild pop concerts or parties, where they dance
in uncontrolled ways*

5

a The growth in the popularity of the car

b particularly with the construction of motorways

c the increased wealth and greater amount of free
time available to young people

Unit 5
Reading and Use of English, page 36

Part 7 Gapped text

1 D **2** C **3** F **4** E **5** G **6** A   B = not used

Vocabulary, page 38

A Adjective and noun collocations

1

1 love **2** feelings **3** couple **4** relationship **5** friend
6 family **7** argument **8** tension

2

1 love-hate **2** pointless **3** unrequited **4** mixed
5 immediate **6** close **7** courting **8** social

B Verbs

1 a called **b** call
2 a fell **b** fell
3 a took **b** takes
4 a turned **b** turn

Language focus, page 39

A Relative clauses

1 who **2** which **3** which **4** whose **5** where **6** why
7 who **8** that/who

B Alternatives to relative clauses

1

1 Venus and Serena Williams – tennis players (Maud
Watson beat her sister Lilian in the first women's final
in 1884).

2 Michael and Ralf Schumacher – Formula 1 racing
drivers

3 The Marx brothers – actors. Groucho (3b), Chico,
Harpo, Zeppo and Gummo

4 Janet and Michael Jackson – popstars. The group
was The Jackson 5 (later The Jacksons).

2

1 b the *one who* won the battle of the sisters

2 a a go-kart *which was* powered by a lawnmower
engine.

  b the first *one who phoned* his mother.

3 a *Monkey Business*, *Duck Soup* and *A Night at the Opera*, all *of which were* released/*which were* all released in the 1930s.

b a moustache *which was* painted on with black greasepaint

4 a Fans *who were* hoping to see Janet

b a group *which comprised* himself and four of his eight brothers and sisters.

Reading and Use of English, page 40

Part 1 Multiple-choice cloze

1 B   2 A   3 D   4 B   5 A   6 D   7 B   8 C

Part 3 Word formation

1 enthusiastically   2 uneasy   3 anxiety   4 breeding
5 recognition   6 dominant (*not* dominating)
7 weight   8 behaviour

Part 4 Key word transformation

1 took/went to (great) pains to keep/stay
2 an instant/instantaneous dislike to
3 tendency to get on
4 he had/he'd known whose it
5 reason why I look
6 Sue would stop looking down

Writing, page 41

Part 1 Essay

2

a The writer talks about the methods referred to as 'punishment' and 'activities'.

b He discusses the use of imprisonment and tougher sentencing. However, he decides this is a less important method because young people may come in contact with more experienced criminals.

c He believes that a more effective way of dealing with antisocial behaviour is by creating more sports facilities and free classes in subjects young people would enjoy.

3

a providing proof:
  evidence suggests that
  a recent survey found that

b stating your own opinion:
  there is no doubt in my mind
  it is therefore my firm belief

c showing causes and results:
  this, in turn, could result in
  is linked to
  could have long-term benefits

d showing contrast:
  However, whereas

4

1 b   2 e   3 a   4 f   5 c   6 d

Unit 6
Reading and Use of English, page 44

Part 8 Multiple matching

1

b The writer reports what the pupils and teachers have said about Henry (for example: undisputed star/soulful eyes/a pupil's best friend/a super dog/a calming influence, etc). She does not use any language to argue or disagree with these descriptions.

2

1 E	2 F	3 B	4 C	5 B
6 D	7 A	8 D	9 F	10 D

Vocabulary, page 46

A Sleep

1 to   2 up   3 through   4 into   5 over   6 on   7 off
8 from

B Abilities

1 d   2 b   3 e   4 a   5 f   6 c

C Adjectives in film reviews

1 unconvincing   2 innovative   3 clichéd   4 gripping
5 over-hyped   6 moving   7 excruciating   8 stunning

Language focus, page 47

1

1 a   2 b   3 b   4 a   5 b

2

1 is understood to be planning a takeover bid for its rival
2 are said (by police) to have taken place on Monday
3 motorcyclist is believed to have been travelling at over 100 mph
4 were thought to be/to have been responsible for the outbreak of flu
5 was alleged to have lied in order to protect her boyfriend
6 my camera stolen last weekend
7 to get/have your eyes tested
8 got my foot stuck in the hole

Reading and Use of English, page 48

Part 2 Open cloze

1 being/getting   2 do   3 only/just/merely
4 themselves   5 which   6 as/being   7 for/without
8 be/get

Part 1 Multiple-choice cloze

1 C   2 B   3 D   4 C   5 A   6 D   7 A   8 C

Part 3 Word formation

1 participants   2 objective   3 distraction
4 significantly   5 memorable   6 unpredictable
7 habitually   8 productivity

Writing, page 50

Part 2 Proposal

1

B is the better answer. It is clearly structured using appropriate headings. The vocabulary is more formal and appropriate for the target readership. For example, the language of suggestion: A uses 'why don't we', 'let's', 'what about'; B uses 'suggest', 'recommend', 'my final proposal'. A doesn't demonstrate a range of vocabulary, e.g. 'really', 'think', etc are repeated. The language and structures in B are more complex, e.g. passive voice (*is required*), participle clause (*requiring*), conditional, modals (*must, should, would*), etc.

2

1 set   **2** would   **3** using   **4** be   **5** to invite

3

<u>Expanding the mind</u>

Debating is an ancient skill and **one that** is equally relevant today. In essence, a debate involves speakers who argue for and against a given proposition. **To do this** successfully **they** must divorce themselves from **their** emotions and **instead** present reasoned arguments in a persuasive style, a **process** requiring meticulous planning. **This said, however**, the debater must be able to deviate from the plan if **they** gauge that **their** arguments are meeting with unexpected success (or otherwise!). **Thus**, the debater is required to think both in advance and on **their** feet, **a combination** that requires a unique form of intellectual dexterity

<u>Student participation</u>

A debating club will be well-attended **if** we promote it in a lively way. To do **this** I suggest that we choose topics **that** are humorous or irreverent **so as to** engage young people. We should **then** put up posters around the college advertising upcoming debates. **In addition**, I recommend posting a short video on the college website showing an example of an entertaining debate. My **final** proposal is awarding prizes to the winner of each event to provide a **further** element of competition.

<u>Conclusion</u>

Debating is a highbrow pastime **that** is enjoyable **so it** would be popular with the students. **As such**, a debating club would be a valuable addition to the college.

Unit 7

Reading and Use of English, page 52

Part 7 Gapped text

1

1 D   **2** E   **3** A   **4** B   **5** G
6 C   F = not used

2

set out – arranged or displayed in writing

set up – started running a business

3

2 b   **3** e   **4** a   **5** g   **6** f   **7** d

Vocabulary, page 54

A Complaints and injuries

1 swollen, sprained, torn
2 blinding, upset, blocked
3 bruised, chipped, dislocated

B Phrasal verbs

1 a come   **b** come
2 a brought   **b** brought
3 a worn   **b** worn
4 a put   **b** put

C Word formation

1

-*en*	*en*-
deafen	encourage
heighten	endanger
deepen	enrich
sadden	enforce
broaden	

2

1 heightened   **2** deepening   **3** encouraging
4 endangered   **5** enforcement   **6** saddened
7 broadens/broadened, enriches/enriched
8 deafening

Language focus, page 55

Reported speech

1

The following words should be crossed out:

1 refused/offered   **2** denied/claimed   **3** accused/complained   **4** persuaded/encouraged
5 complimented/congratulated   **6** suggested/argued
7 urge/convince   **8** told/assured   **9** suggested/proposed   **10** ordered/insisted

2

1 a he would cut   **b** to cut
2 a thought I should take   **b** (that) I (should) take/ (that) I took

3 a they had to leave   **b** them to leave
4 a he had always loved   **b** having always loved

5 a hadn't stolen it   **b** having stolen it/
stealing it

6 a was paid   **b** to have been paid

7 a she could take   **b** his name (should)
not

8 a had been abducted   **b** have been abducted

Reading and Use of English, page 57

Part 1 Multiple-choice cloze

1 B **2** D **3** C **4** D **5** A **6** B **7** A **8** C

Part 2 Open cloze

1 do **2** are **3** these **4** either **5** before **6** not **7** If
8 until/till

Part 4   Key word transformation

1 hugely beneficial to us if

2 to have a significant effect on

3 objected to his photograph being/objected to
having his photograph

4 insisted on giving

5 I should have/(that) I have the operation on

6 formal complaint, they agreed to look

Writing, page 58

Part 2 Review

2

Yes

3

1 title **2** performance **3** nomination **4** set
5 scenes **6** climax **7** score **8** action **9** insight
10 lines

4

extremely powerful acting performance

well-deserved Oscar nomination

the boxing scenes are entirely convincing

(the film builds up to) a dramatic climax

(Michael Mann's) expert direction

the moving musical score

(one of the most) memorable moments (of the film)

(it provides) a fascinating insight (into)

witty lines

5

is reason enough to see the film

don't be put off if you're not a boxing fan

There's something for everyone in the film

will have you laughing out loud

Unit 8

Reading and Use of English, page 60

Part 5 Multiple choice

1

1 D   **2** D   **3** C   **4** A   **5** C   **6** B

2

1 c   **2** a   **3** b

3

1 H   **2** D   **3** H   **4** H   **5** D

4

a underhand **b** devious **c** reputable **d** candid
e straight

Vocabulary, page 62

A Verbs formed with *up, down, over* and *under*

1

1 uphear **2** overgo **3** underroot **4** uprule
5 downhold

2

1 uphold/overrule **2** undergo **3** update/upgrade
4 undercut **5** downplay

B Adjectives formed with *in, off, on, out* and *over*

1 oncoming **2** ongoing **3** outlying **4** off-duty
5 inborn

C Plans

1

1 emergency **2** devious **3** impracticable **4** carry
out **5** put forward **6** shelve

2

1 impracticable **2** emergency **3** devious **4** shelved
5 carrying out **6** put forward

D Amount

1 d **2** f **3** a **4** e **5** b **6** c

Language focus, page 64

A Talking about the future

1 C   **2** C   **3** B   **4** C   **5** D
6 C   **7** A   **8** B

B Determiners

1 no other **2** every other **3** Every few **4** another
two **5** quite a few/quite a lot of **6** quite some
7 not much **8** some three

Reading and Use of English, page 65

Part 2 Open cloze

1 the **2** in(to) **3** for **4** Although/Though/While/
Whilst/Whereas **5** by **6** its **7** us **8** to

Part 3 Word formation

1 undergone **2** undoubtedly/doubtlessly

3 inaccuracy/inaccuracies **4** significant
5 irresistibly **6** threatening **7** tendency
8 productivity/production

Part 4 Key word transformation

1 on no fewer than **2** is second to none when **3** the most of the conference by **4** you would turn down
5 lose his temper for no **6** will/can be installed at no extra/additional

Writing, page 67

Part 1 Essay

2

1 concern **2** claims **3** coverage **4** status
5 resources **6** action **7** importance

Unit 9

Reading and Use of English, page 68

Part 6 Cross-text multiple matching

1

1 D

A … *in her latest work she does not disappoint.*

B … *this one is worthy of the same volume of praise.*

C … *but it has turned out to be a risk worth taking.*

D … *there is a sense of inconsequentiality.*

2 A

A *Although Windham cannot claim this approach as hers alone, …*

C *The idea of the set piece (rather than continuous narrative) owes much to* In Patagonia, *the seminal work of travel writer Bruce Chatwin.*

3 B

A … *employing a frankness about her own occasional naivety which puts her in situations of jeopardy.*

B Sentences 1–4

C … *unlike Chatwin's fictionalized anecdotes of real people and places, Windham gives us an undistorted account of her interactions with characters from all walks of life …*

D … *none of these encounters lacks vividness or authenticity, …*

4 B

B *It is her eye for fine detail and her ability to describe it in ways that convince the reader that the memories are their own …*

D … *her pen becomes a paint brush that conveys the shades and hues, the light and the dark of her subjects, and the reader is fully present in the experience.*

2

1 turned **2** on **3** set **4** across **5** one **6** for

Vocabulary, page 70

A Describing an adventure

1

1 set **2** ran **3** rang **4** turned **5** won **6** kicked

2

1 gruelling **2** arid **3** intrepid **4** swirling **5** idyllic

B Criticism

1

1 constructive **2** valid **3** upset by **4** arouse
5 respond to **6** draw

2

1 A   **2** B   **3** D   **4** C

C Word formation

1

1 supporting **2** composure **3** entry **4** hardship
5 identity

2

1 winning entry **2** Supporting Actor **3** a case of mistaken identity **4** regained his composure
5 caused considerable hardship

Language focus, page 71

Creating emphasis

1

1 have **2** what **3** because **4** and **5** it **6** so

Reading and Use of English, page 72

Part 1 Multiple-choice cloze

1 B **2** B **3** D **4** C **5** D **6** B **7** B **8** A

Part 2 Open cloze

1 no/little **2** those **3** for **4** unless **5** By **6** have
7 from **8** since

Part 3 Word formation

1 safety **2** handful **3** consultant **4** enabled
5 uninhibited **6** readily **7** deterrent **8** temptation

Part 4 Key word transformation

1 only when we were in/reached the

2 is all (that) Steve ever talks

3 wasn't/was not until we ('d/had) arrived

4 while I was having a look

5 it turned out to

6 into a heated argument

Writing, page 74

Part 2 Report

2

1 F **2** T **3** F **4** T **5** F

3

1 poor **2** likely **3** unqualified **4** destructive
5 prosperous

Unit 10

Reading and Use of English, page 76

Part 5 Multiple choice

1

1 B **2** D **3** A **4** C **5** A **6** B

Vocabulary, page 78

1

A		B	
1	owl	**1**	stomach
2	mouse	**2**	leaves
3	bee	**3**	drum
4	dog	**4**	music
5	lion	**5**	floorboards

2

1 C	**2** A	**3** B	**4** D	**5** D
6 B	**7** D	**8** A	**9** B	**10** D

Language focus, page 79

Participle clauses

1 *Lord of the Rings: Return of the King* won 11 Oscars, *equalling* the record held by *Ben Hur* and *Titanic* for the highest number of Academy Awards.

2 *Having* finally *discovered* where the leak was, we called in a plumber.

3 The school now has 1254 students, *representing* a six per cent increase on last year's figure.

4 Part of the stadium roof collapsed, *injuring* six spectators.

5 *Not being* a parent, I can take my holidays whenever I like.

6 The team has had a disastrous season so far, *winning/having won* only three of its last sixteen games.

7 Our parents *having gone* away for the weekend, my brother and I had a party.

8 *Walking* home from school yesterday, I bumped into Alex.

Reading and Use of English, page 79

Part 2 Open cloze

1 not **2** with **3** one **4** having **5** whereas/while/whilst **6** in **7** which **8** no/little

Part 1 Multiple-choice cloze

1 C **2** D **3** B **4** D **5** D **6** C **7** A **8** C

Part 3 Word formation

1 guaranteed **2** Costing **3** fitted **4** uninterrupted **5** luxurious **6** equipped **7** running **8** permission

Part 4 Key word transformation

1 wishing/wanting to let down

2 come to/made/taken/reached the/a decision to

3 to keep an eye on

4 is bound to be a change

5 to take/accept responsibility for

6 suggested (that) we get rid of/suggested we should get rid of

Writing, page 82

Part 1 Essay

2

might motivate, for want of, as a result, in this way, would subsequently provide, would generate opportunities

3

1 confirmed **2** ignored **3** forgotten **4** misrepresented **5** condemned **6** applauded

Unit 11

Reading and Use of English, page 84

Part 8 Multiple matching

1

1 B **2** E **3** D **4** B **5** C **6** D **7** A **8** D **9** A **10** C

2

1 inspiration **2** alongside **3** benefit **4** hooked **5** blown **6** associated **7** interest **8** take

Vocabulary, page 86

A Sight

1 visibility **2** eyesight, vision **3** eye **4** look **5** sight **6** full **7** closer **8** naked **9** keep **10** catch

B *Read* and *write*

1

1 off **2** up **3** out **4** into

2

a 4 **b** 2 **c** 1 **d** 3

Language focus, page 87

Inversion

1

1 no **2** have **3** are **4** but **5** Not **6** Under **7** when/if **8** will/can **9** Only **10** On

2

Suggested answers:

1 had I got **2** she saw **3** have I had **4** will I allow **5** had he started **6** did I think **7** will I follow/take **8** did they realize/know

Reading and Use of English, page 88

Part 1 Multiple-choice cloze

1 C **2** B **3** D **4** A **5** B **6** C **7** C **8** A

Part 3 Word formation

1 environmental **2** specialized **3** depth **4** insight
5 perceptions **6** advising **7** encourages/encouraged
8 independent

Part 4 Key word transformation

1 off/out than we caught sight
2 in spite of being/having been brought
3 closer look (at it) did we
4 to/would be such a low/poor/small turnout
5 with being in the public eye
6 sure/certain your valuables are kept out

Writing, page 90

Part 2 Formal email

2

college, student leader, tertiary institution,
undergraduates, vocational and academic courses,
science and technology, sister school, related
subjects, academic tradition

3

1 although **2** additionally **3** and at the same time
4 none possible **5** as since **6** in addition/what is more

4

1 However/On the other hand **2** but **3** While/In
spite of the fact that **4** so **5** therefore/as a result
6 Moreover/In addition/Furthermore **7** In spite of
the fact that **8** Despite

Unit 12

Reading and Use of English, page 92

Part 7 Gapped text

1

1 G **2** E **3** B **4** F **5** C
6 A **D** = not used

2

1 tap, sparkling **2** drinking **3** rain **4** salt
5 running **6** flood

Vocabulary, page 94

A Attitude adverbials

1 ridiculously **2** worryingly **3** unusually **4** Funnily
5 laughably **6** understandably

B Collocations with *work*

1 conservation work **2** consultancy work **3** work
experience **4** work permit **5** social work
6 restoration work **7** casual work **8** work incentive

C Approximation

1a

a Some **b** roughly **c** Upwards

2

1 something **2** so **3** Very **4** Just **5** round
6 upwards **7** some **8** something

Language focus, page 95

A Conjunctions

Suggested answers:

1 I enjoyed the film *Ali* even though I don't like
boxing.
2 They won the game despite the fact that two of
their players were sent off.
3 We'd better/We ought to phone her, otherwise she'll
worry about us.
4 However I comb my hair, it always looks a mess!
5 I'll leave the plate there in case you want some
more later.
6 We spoke very quietly so as not to wake up my dad.

B Modal verbs

1 permitted **2** forbidden **3** recommended
4 required **5** obliged **6** supposed **7** presumed
8 obligatory

Reading and Use of English, page 96

Part 1 Multiple-choice cloze

1 D **2** A **3** A **4** B **5** C **6** B **7** D **8** C

Part 2 Open cloze

1 what **2** there **3** which **4** to **5** but **6** so
7 without **8** the

Part 3 Word formation

1 knowledge **2** discovery **3** intensifies **4** erosion
5 unreliable **6** threatened **7** endangered **8** survival

Part 4 Key word transformation

1 in perfect/full working order
2 in case the shops run/sell
3 otherwise tigers/the tiger could/may/might die/be
wiped
4 not knowing/speaking a single word/bit of
5 never to have lent
6 manager unless you work on/at your

Writing, page 98

Part 2 Proposal

1

1 This has led to **2** therefore **3** also **4** instead
5 Whilst **6** As well as **7** Clearly **8** Finally
9 In order to **10** as

2

*A substantial proportion of the budget should therefore
be allocated to*

Money might also be spent on

funds would also need to be set aside for

some of the budget should be devoted to

Unit 13
Reading and Use of English, page 100

Part 6 Cross-text multiple matching

1

1 A

A ... *evident in the modern world is that, religion aside, people will choose to reject certain foods to mark social boundaries; class, wealth, ethical viewpoint, and so on.*

B ... *religion is still central in governing what is regarded as fit to be consumed, or not.*

C *Foods considered sacred and taboo have been defined by religion; ...*

D ... *in most cases, the exclusion of foods from a diet continues to be a deliberate act of worship.*

2 B

B ... *the 'audience' was not peripheral. Rather it was their unification which was the goal of the shared meal.*

D *In sharing a meal, we reinforce the ties that bind us to family, friends, associates, or even larger social groups.*

3 C

A ... *no longer is there a necessity to partake of a meal in a wider group setting.*

B *Even until the last century, the tradition of younger generations returning to the matriarchal home for the ritual weekly gathering and grandmother's cooking was still prevalent. It seems, rather sadly, that this has been abandoned, perhaps in favour of other pursuits.*

C *There appears to be a resurgence of interest in the concept of cooking and providing for the larger group; ...*

D *And as the craftsmanship involved with food continues to die out, so do the celebrations that bring people together. Must we be doomed to a life of flavoured pills eaten in self-inflicted solitary confinement?*

4 D

C ... *we have developed a hasty and mechanical approach to the making of meals ...*

D ... *the meals that you make ready for yourself, or which have been made ready for you, have been produced with little thought and attention.*

2

1 explained as   **2** later did   **3** no means   **4** favour of   **5** What is   **6** no less   **7** a good   **8** so do

Vocabulary, page 102

A Phrasal verbs and prepositions

a Eating and drinking

1 off   **2** down   **3** at   **4** up

b Deception

1 into   **2** on   **3** at   **4** for

B Expressions with *eat*

1

1 home   **2** hand   **3** profits   **4** words   **5** horse   **6** bird

2

2 a   **3** f   **4** b   **5** e   **6** d

C Intensifiers

1 b   **2** e   **3** f   **4** h   **5** d   **6** a   **7** g   **8** c

Language focus, page 103

Comparisons

1 ... I worked as a security guard ...

2 ... attracted her to him as/but his warm ...

3 ... anywhere near as hard ...

4 ... a great deal more convenient ...

5 ... the film was so hugely successful ...

6 ... the same way as certain types ...

Reading and Use of English, page 104

Part 1 Multiple-choice cloze

1 C   **2** D   **3** B   **4** C   **5** C   **6** A   **7** B   **8** B

Part 2 Open cloze

1 it/this   **2** While/Whilst/Although/Though **3** everyone   **4** behind   **5** despite   **6** becoming/being **7** by   **8** them

Part 3 Word formation

1 imaginative   **2** proof   **3** unattractive **4** refreshingly   **5** combinations   **6** heights **7** encouraging   **8** fussiest

Part 4 Key word transformation

1 up a big/an appetite during   **2** much in what you say as   **3** close second to the   **4** of independence, in contrast to   **5** was nowhere near as spicy   **6** you fell for such a

Writing, page 106

Part 1 Essay

2

1 preferable   **2** establishment   **3** were   **4** having **5** to give   **6** As soon as   **7** is   **8** could be

Unit 14
Reading and Use of English, page 108

Part 5 Multiple choice

1 B   **2** C   **3** C   **4** D   **5** A   **6** A

Vocabulary, page 110

A Money

1 counterfeit   **2** pocket   **3** housekeeping   **4** ransom **5** redundancy   **6** sponsorship

B Verbs usually associated with money

1

1 C   **2** B   **3** C   **4** A   **5** D

2

1 pay   **2** owe   **3** lend   **4** save   **5** borrow

3

1 owe, an apology   **2** pay, respects   **3** borrowed, word   **4** owed, a favour   **5** paying, a compliment

Language focus, page 111

Noun phrases

1

1 sign   **2** matter   **3** grain, pack   **4** sense   **5** state   **6** source   **7** depths, height   **8** chances

2

1 bottle of water   **2** door handle   **3** a scrap of evidence   **4** pieces of advice   **5** three-page essay   **6** a week's work   **7** mountain tops   **8** last April's edition

Reading and Use of English, page 112

Part 2 Open cloze

1 if/though   **2** to   **3** there   **4** in   **5** one   **6** out   **7** spite   **8** being

Part 3 Word formation

1 deception   **2** contestant   **3** trial   **4** numerous   **5** unsure   **6** strategically   **7** recording   **8** dishonesty

Part 4 Key word transformation

1 it if you paid/would pay/could pay in

2 to be no sign of

3 chances of survival/surviving are thought/seem/ appear

4 had felt/experienced/had (had) a sense of achievement

5 with a regular source/means

6 making/having made the purchase on

Writing, page 114

Part 2 Proposal

Task 1

1

1 c   **2** a   **3** d   **4** f   **5** b   **6** e

2

1 price   **2** technology   **3** design   **4** money   **5** service   **6** warranty

Task 2

1

appreciative   constructive   polite   reasonable   concise   persuasive

2

1 large number, enthusiastic   **2** am confident, conducted   **3** Perhaps there could be, allow

students to   **4** investing in, unsatisfactory   **5** begin construction of

3

1 suited   **2** short   **3** complete

Task 3

1 stroll, b   **2** soak, e   **3** splash, a   **4** hike, d   **5** take, c

Listening bank

Unit 1, page 116

Listening Part 1   **Multiple choice**

1 B   **2** A   **3** A   **4** C   **5** B   **6** C

Unit 2, page 117

Listening Part 2   **Sentence completion**

1 clear details   **2** soft edges   **3** desert   **4** traditional values   **5** (popular) magazines   **6** emotional response   **7** value   **8** information

Unit 3, page 118

Listening Part 3   **Multiple choice**

1 B   **2** A   **3** C   **4** B   **5** D   **6** C

Unit 4, page 119

Listening Part 4   **Multiple matching**

1 H   **2** G   **3** D   **4** A   **5** F   **6** E   **7** B   **8** H   **9** D   **10** A

Unit 5, page 120

Listening Part 1   **Multiple choice**

1 C   **2** A   **3** A   **4** B   **5** A   **6** C

Unit 6, page 121

Listening Part 2   **Sentence completion**

1 social functions   **2** beggars   **3** genetic   **4** ignore   **5** introverts   **6** memories   **7** information technology/ IT   **8** training courses

Unit 7, page 122

Listening Part 3   **Multiple choice**

1 B   **2** D   **3** A   **4** B   **5** C   **6** D

Unit 8, page 123

Listening Part 4   **Multiple matching**

1 E   **2** C   **3** H   **4** A   **5** G   **6** A   **7** F   **8** H   **9** D   **10** C

Unit 9, page 124

Listening Part 3   **Multiple choice**

1 B   **2** D   **3** A   **4** D   **5** C   **6** B

Unit 10, page 125

Listening Part 4   **Multiple matching**

1 D   **2** F   **3** A   **4** G   **5** B   **6** E   **7** H   **8** G   **9** B   **10** F

Unit 11, page 126

Listening Part 1   **Multiple choice**
1 B   2 C   3 A   4 C   5 B   6 A

Unit 12, page 127

Listening Part 2   **Sentence completion**
1 (family) farm   **2** (native) trees   **3** rats   **4** (walking) tracks   **5** (wire) fences   **6** (plant) nursery   **7** birds, insects   **8** seeds

Unit 13, page 128

Listening Part 1   **Multiple choice**
1 C   2 B   3 A   4 B   5 C   6 A

Unit 14, page 129

Listening Part 3   **Multiple choice**
1 A   2 B   3 D   4 B   5 C   6 A

MACMILLAN DICTIONARY

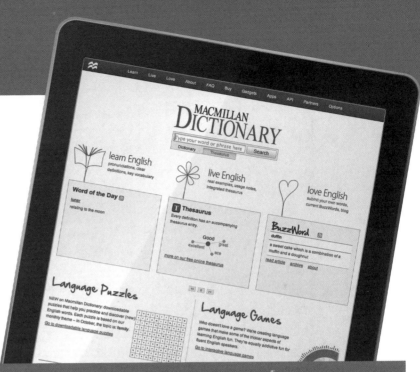

Macmillan Dictionary Online

Free online **dictionary** and **thesaurus**.

The essential tool for every learner of English

- Free online dictionary in British and American English with integrated thesaurus

- Red words and star ratings highlight the 7,500 words that make up the core vocabulary of English

- Includes audio pronunciation of all headwords

- Other language resources include: games, videos and lesson plans

- Keep up to date with the Word of the Day, BuzzWord articles and Open Dictionary

- Join our language community on social media and our language blog:

www.macmillandictionary.com